© 1977
(U.K.)

# Practical Gem
# Testing

© 1977 (U.K.)

# PRACTICAL GEM TESTING

### David Lewis FGA

N.A.G. Press Limited, London

Published in 1977

© N.A.G. Press Ltd (U.K.)
(in conjunction with
Northwood Publications Ltd)
and David Lewis, 1977

ISBN 7198 0041 2

Typeset by Quickset Ltd, London.
Printed and bound in Great Britain
by T. & A. Constable Ltd, Edinburgh.

# CONTENTS

© 1977 (U.K.)

# PREFACE

During a decade of attending the Trent Polytechnic part-time course on gemmology, initially as a student and then as instructor, I formed the opinion that the majority of students, when attempting to identify gemstones, had difficulty (a) in deciding which tests to apply to any particular gem species to achieve rapid and positive identification, (b) in knowing what order to carry out the tests, and (c) in being able to find the tests relating to each gemstone fully described in the various textbooks on gemmology.

In this book I have attempted to set out the tests in a clear and straightforward order in the hope that students of gemmology will benefit from my own experience in gem testing.

I am grateful to Dr. Eduard Gübelin for supplying some of the superb photographs of inclusions, to Eric Bruton and the late Robert Webster for their willing help and advice in the preparation of the manuscript, to David Smalley for his work on inclusion photography, and to Brian Scorer for reading the manuscript and offering suggestions.

I am further indebted to all the great gemmologists of the past and present who have paved the way to this book by laying the foundations of gem testing technique by their assiduous research. I hope that this addition to gemmological literature will be received as it was intended, not as a work to advance the science of gemmology, but as one to make gemstone identification available to a wider group of people.

Nottingham, 1977                                     David Lewis

# INTRODUCTION

The purpose of this handbook is to provide guidance to the reader who wishes to identify the most commonly encountered gemstones in the quickest and surest manner. The book is so designed that a person with little gemmological experience can follow the instructions and carry out gem-testing, although it must be pointed out at the outset that practice with the instruments is necessary before any degree of proficiency can be obtained.

It is hoped that the book will be of interest to the following groups of people in particular:—

1. Professional jewellers, or others, who wish to be able to identify gemstones but do not have the time or the inclination to make a fuller study of gemmology, which requires the gaining of a lot of theoretical knowledge, much of which is of little practical benefit.

2. Students of gemmology who require guidance on the practical aspects of gem-testing, set out in a concise and easy-to-follow manner.

3. Those who have passed the examinations but now find that a further step has to be taken before they have the proficiency and experience to call themselves 'gemmologists'.

It is impossible to identify the majority of gemstones without the availability of certain gem testing instruments and the proficiency to use them to obtain the best results, so the first section of the book is devoted to describing the instruments to obtain and the best methods of using them.

Emphasis is placed on methods suitable for identifying gemstones which are set in some form of jewellery, and for this reason specific gravity as a testing method has been mostly ignored, but it is assumed that light may be transmitted through the back of the setting, and that the setting does not preclude placing the largest flat facet of the stone on the refractometer. Stones in closed back settings are more difficult and in certain cases the stone may have to be removed from its setting to facilitate positive identification.

It is assumed that the reader is familiar with the names, colour and general appearance of the majority of gemstones found in jewellery, although even this knowledge is not a complete prerequisite for using the book as there is a section devoted to identifying gemstones from scratch, without colour and appearance being taken into account in the initial stages.

The series of tests described to facilitate the identification of each particular type of gemstone are not intended to be totally foolproof, but are offered more as a guide, as there are always new developments in the manufacture of synthetic and imitation stones and it is always possible that one of these will render a test, which up to that time was thought to be foolproof, totally useless in respect to the gemstone concerned.

It may be well to mention here that scientists of the present age are capable of manufacturing virtually any gemstone in their laboratories. The only things that prevent even more synthetic stones than there are already from appearing on the market are the facts that in many cases it costs more to produce the synthetic than it does to obtain the natural material, therefore making manufacture an uncommercial proposition, and that there is not enough demand for the less popular gemstones to warrant production of them synthetically on a commercial scale. However there must always be borne in the mind the possibility of a lesser known synthetic turning up, perhaps one made for experiment and then released on the market for devilment.

# Part 1

# THE GEM-TESTING LABORATORY

The identification of gemstones is based upon the principle that each particular type of gemstone possesses certain characteristics that are peculiar to that type alone.

It is a characteristic of diamond that it is harder than any other gemstone. If, therefore, a stone which is thought to be diamond is carefully tested by drawing a pointed part of its surface firmly across a polished surface of a piece of corundum (i.e. either ruby or sapphire), which is the next hardest gem material, it may be safely identified as diamond if it leaves an incision on the corundum, as there is no other gem species hard enough to do this.

This characteristic of diamond is only quoted as an explanatory example, and it is to be hoped that the reader, armed with his first piece of gem-testing knowledge, will not at this stage close the book and go dashing about testing all available colourless stones in this way. Apart from ruining a perfectly good piece of corundum by leaving scratch marks all over it, the chances are that a number of harmless softer stones will also be damaged. On top of this the prospective gemmologist will be making use of a testing method which is, thankfully, almost obsolete.

The proof of possession of a single characteristic is not generally sufficient information on its own to identify a gemstone; more often it is necessary to build up a series of positive tests before identification can be assured.

To obtain all the relevant data requires the use of certain instruments, most of which have been designed specially for the gemmologist. These are now described along with advice as to their most efficient use.

## WHITE LIGHT SOURCE

As the majority of the gem-testing techniques are optical, a good bright light source is essential. The professional versions are known as "intensity lamps", and employ condensers to provide bright narrow beams of light.

Ideally it should be possible to direct the beam of light in any direction, and to be able to graduate it from intense to weak at will. An inbuilt diaphragm (a little gadget like a shutter, which can be closed a little at a time so as to provide a beam of any diameter) is extremely useful, especially when working with the spectroscope (see relevant section).

Also available should be an Anglepoise type of light source, of the kind commonly in use in jewellers' shops.

## STONE TONGS

Although the book is aimed towards the identification of gemstones which are set in some form of jewellery, the gemmologist is often called upon to work with loose material. The handling and examination of such stones is carried out far more easily with the use of specially made tweezers called stone tongs.

The most practical type of instrument is about 5in. to 6in. long with fairly wide, rounded tips. The tongs with narrow, pointed tips look far more professional but it is much easier to lose gemstones with them. The tips are grooved inside to obtain a better grip on the stone than would be possible with smooth tongs.

The correct method to pick up the stone is to place it on a surface with its table facet (the top facet of a gemstone) down, i.e. the stone is upside down. Hold the tongs with forefinger and thumb, so that the tips of the tongs are placed either side of the stone and resting on the surface. The tongs at this point should be almost parallel to the surface.

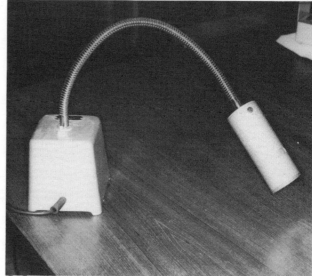

The intensity lamp is valuable for splitting a bright spot of light when using certain instruments. This one splits cold light through a glass fibre element which can be moved in any position. It is particularly useful when using a spectroscope.

A less expensive intensity lamp which has an adjustable diaphragm and is primarily intended for use with a microscope.

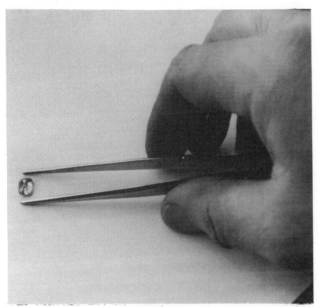

(Above) A polished gem should be placed on its table on a flat surface before picking it up with gem tongs.

So-called "diamond tongs" which grip the stone by three prongs.

A high quality 10x lens corrected for gemmology work.

Light but firm pressure by the thumb and finger will now bring the tips of the tongs into contact with the girdle (i.e. the sides) of the gemstone, at which point it may be lifted from the surface and manipulated as necessary. Too much finger pressure may cause the stone to "flirt" out of the tongs and be lost. The grip must be firm, but also gentle.

It is quite useful to have available a similar pair of tongs but with a metal slide attachment which will lock the stone into position for lengthy examination with less hand fatigue. These tongs are generally heavier and a little more difficult to manipulate, but are of occasional benefit.

The correct method of use with such tongs is to pick up the stone exactly as described above, and then, when you have satisfied yourself that a suitable grip has been obtained on the stone, to ease the slide firmly into position.

An instrument composed of a set of three wire tongs, contained in a tube about four or five inches long, which extend from the tube when a button at its top end is depressed with the thumb, can also prove useful. These are sometimes called "diamond tongs".

The stone to be examined should be placed table facet down and then gripped by the tongs around the girdle. Care should then be taken to see that the stone is safely gripped by the tongs by easing it into position with the fingers, before examination is carried out.

## 10x LENSES

The initial examination of a gemstone is carried out by normal, unaided vision, during which the general appearance, colour, lustre (i.e. the quality of surface reflection), condition and possible identity of the stone may be assessed.

Following this a more detailed examination of the stone than is possible with the naked eye alone may be desired, and it is necessary to use some form of magnification.

The standard instrument for carrying out this work is one

which will increase the apparent size of the stone by ten times (generally indicated by 10x).

There are two basic types of instrument available: the pocket lens, which is attached by a swivel fitting to a protective housing so that it may be folded up and carried about in the pocket without causing damage to the lens, and the loupe which may be held in the eye like a monocle, so leaving both hands free to manipulate the stone.

The pocket lens is by far the most popular of the two instruments with gemmologists and stone dealers generally, but the author has to admit to a preference for the loupe. The fact that both hands are free from holding the lens makes it well worth the trouble of obtaining a suitable instrument and learning how to hold it in the eye. Perhaps the ideal gemmologist will possess both types.

Whether it is pocket lens or loupe that is decided upon, the important thing is that it definitely magnifies the object by 10x (most instruments are stamped with the magnification power), and that it is a lens of good quality. To assist in choosing an instrument, the following points should be borne in mind.

A 10x loupe suitable for the examination of gem materials.

## ON CHOOSING A 10x LENS OR LOUPE

Examine a piece of graph paper with the lens and check the following indications of the instruments quality.

1. All the lines in the area of vision through the lens should be in focus at one time. If any of the lines are blurred, curved or wider around the edges of vision than in the centre, then the lens is of inferior quality.
2. You should be able to keep all the lines in focus with ease.
3. The lines should appear "clean" and sharp. If they are edged by a colour fringe, the lens is of inferior quality and not suitable for gemmological use.

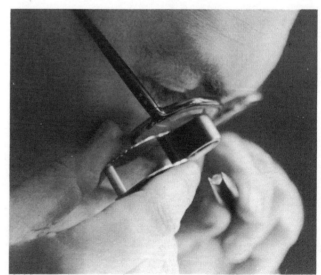

The lens should be placed close to the eye when examining a gem stone.

6

# HOW TO USE THE 10x LENS AND LOUPE

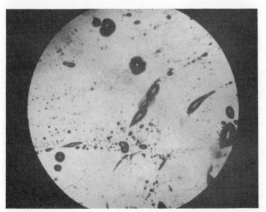

Once the art of placing the loupe on the eye is mastered, both hands are left free.

Inclusions, like this, in paste (glass gem) may often be identified with a lens or loupe.

A light source should be positioned in front of the forehead, pointing towards the chest, and the stone to be examined brought to about one inch away from the lens and into focus. The illustration shows how a pocket lens should be held when looking at a stone. The hands should rest against each other to steady them.

It is a good thing to have room for manoeuvre so that you are able to have the light source to one side, or even pointing over your shoulder, should that be required.

The knack of holding the loupe in the eye may be gained quite simply. Press the lower edge of the eyepiece down into the skin just below the eye without altering your normal facial expression. Then lift the upper eyebrow slightly and wedge the top edge of the loupe into the skin above the eye. By then closing the eyebrow on top of it, the loupe will be held firmly in position.

An account of some of the uses of the 10x lens will give an idea of its importance and emphasise the necessity of obtaining good quality instruments.

The examination of a gemstone's surface with the 10x lens can often be of value.

Example *a*. Diamond may be separated from its simulants by noting the high surface reflection (lustre) of its surface and the sharp join between facet edges.

Example *b*. Imitation gemstones called doublets or triplets (composite stones made of two or three pieces of material cemented or fused together) may be identified as such with the lens, the join marks between the substances being easily seen. Composite stones imitating sapphire and emerald are extremely common.

Even more information may be obtained by examining the internal features of gemstones as most of them contain growth features (called inclusions), which help in their identification.

7

Example *a*. Natural and synthetic sapphires and rubies contain inclusions which may be seen with the lens and are essential towards identification.

Example *b*. Hessonite and demantoid garnets contain inclusions which are so distinctive that these stones may be identified with the use of the 10x lens alone.

Example *c*. Glass imitation stones contain internal features which are often sufficient to prove their identity.

The examination of the internal features of gemstones with the 10x lens may be carried out more easily by employing one of the following methods.

1. When examining the stone, hold a piece of bright white card behind it and arrange the light source so that most of light falls directly upon the card, rather than the stone. It will be found that many inclusions stand out much better against this white background.

2. Inclusions are often more easily seen when viewed through the side of the stone or through the back. With set stones in fact, it is often best to look through the back of the setting and view the stone against a white background.

3. Inclusions are often difficult to see because the gemstone reflects quite a high proportion of light from its surface, therefore restricting the amount of vision into the stone. To eliminate this surface reflection and make looking into the stone easier the gem may be immersed in a liquid of a similar refractive index. Refractive index is explained later under the heading, THE REFRACTOMETER.

The principle is that the nearer the refractive index of the liquid is to the stone the easier it will be to see into the stone, but it will be found that almost any colourless liquid, even water, will make viewing inclusions much easier.

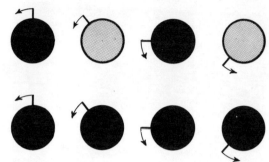

(Top right across two pages) How a doubly refractive gem becomes light and dark by rotation in a polariscope.
(Bottom row across two pages) A singly refractive gem will remain dark all the time during rotation in the polariscope.

If a stone is immersed in water or a liquid of higher refractive index in a glass cell, the inclusions are easier to see with a lens or microscope.

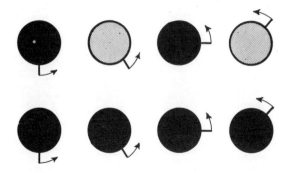

The gemstone should be placed in a small glass cell which contains enough liquid to cover the stone and then examined, again against a white background and illuminated by a strong light source. If water is used it will be found quite useful to fill a white-walled cup and immerse the stone in this. Holding the stone just under the surface and viewing with the lens often brings surprisingly good results. (The light source should be directed into the cup).

Colour zoning — bands of colour — in both natural and synthetic sapphires is generally best seen with the 10x lens while the stone immersed in one of these ways.

## THE POLARISCOPE

The polariscope is an instrument for determining whether a stone is singly refractive to light (i.e. light travels through the stone as a single ray), or doubly refractive (i.e. light is split into two on entering the stone and travels through it as two separate rays).

When it is considered that diamond, garnet, spinel, fluorspar, opal and the glasses are all singly refractive, whereas amongst the doubly refractive stones are ruby, sapphire, emerald, zircon, topaz, chrysoberyl, tourmaline and quartz, it will be realised that the polariscope provides a quick and easy test for eliminating many possible identities of a gemstone.

Example. If a blue stone, thought to be sapphire, was tested on the polariscope and found to be singly refractive, then that test would immediately eliminate the possibility of the stone being a sapphire, as sapphires are always doubly refractive. Further, the test would suggest that the stone would be either spinel or glass, as these are the only singly refractive substances commonly found in sapphire blue colour.

A table polariscope with the light source contained in the base, which is one of the most convenient to use.

# CHOOSING A POLARISCOPE

A table polariscope with an inbuilt light source, as illustrated, is to be recommended.

For those on a tight budget it is possible to make a polariscope quite simply by obtaining two pieces of polaroid and fixing them as panels at opposite ends of a box big enough to leave about 4in. clearance between the polaroids, then cutting two sides of the box away so that the stone may be inserted by hand.

This home-made polariscope may be held over a light source and should work quite satisfactorily.

The polaroids must be held in the correct orientation to each other i.e. in the "crossed" position. This may be found out by holding them close together and turning one of them until the least possible amount of light passes through them. As a check, a known doubly refractive stone may be tested between them to make sure the correct effect is obtained as explained in 2 below.

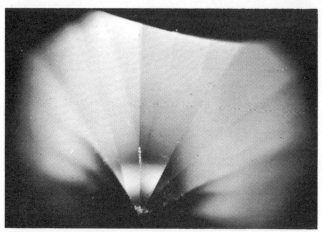

Anomalous double refraction or tabby extinction which can occur in singly refractive materials under stress. The picture above shows a synthetic spinel between the polaroids. The picture below shows the same stone after the polaroids are crossed.

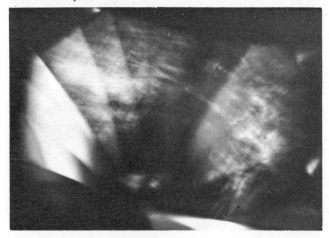

# ON USING THE POLARISCOPE

The method of testing is to hold the stone between the upper and lower polaroids and to rotate it while viewing the effect through the upper filter. Provided that a reasonable light source is shining from underneath the instrument towards the eye, the stone will react in one of the following ways.

1. The stone will be completely dark throughout a complete rotation.

This result proves the stone to be singly refractive provided that the stone has been tested in all directions and the same result has always been obtained.

A D-I-Y polariscope made with two pieces of polaroid which has a battery operated light source. A simpler variation can be made simply with crossed pieces of polaroid.

The standard Rayner refractometer, which reads up to an R.I. of 1.81 using the usual refractive liquid.

2. During a complete rotation the stone changes from dark to light four times.

This proves the stone to be doubly refractive.

3. There are a number of intermediary effects which may confuse the beginner.

*a.* An effect that may be described as a number of black shadows irregularly arranged through the stone, which move about when the stone is turned. This has been called "tabby extinction" because of the likeness of the effect to the markings on a tabby cat, and is typical of synthetic spinels and some synthetic corundum.

*b.* Some glass imitation stones exhibit a cross-like shadow across the stone which retains its position, in relationship to the polariscope, when the stone is turned. This effect is typical of glass and is quite a good indication of the identity of a stone.

*c.* Diamonds exhibit an indistinctive effect, sometimes called anomalous double refraction, of a delicate mottled shadow, which moves about the stone when it is turned and may suggest the presence of double refraction. As the polariscope is largely ignored when testing possible diamonds, this effect should not cause much confusion.

*d.* Some garnets show a distinct doubly refractive effect when tested on the polariscope. Here again the identification of these stones is generally carried out without the use of the polariscope so the effect should not cause great concern.

## THE REFRACTOMETER

Light travels through air, in straight lines, at a speed of approximately 186,000 miles per second.

When light enters a gemstone it is slowed down, and if it

enters at an angle, it is thrown off course as it passes through the stone's surface. This deviation of light is called refraction.

As the speed of light through some gemstones is reduced by a greater amount than through others, so also the amount of refraction or bending varies proportionately, depending on the gemstone concerned.

It has been found possible to measure the amount of refraction of light passing from air into a gemstone, and to quote this measurement in figures called the stone's refractive index (abbreviated to R.I.). Refraction of light is constant for any substance, i.e. all substances of identical structure and composition have the same R.I., and virtually all substances of differing structure and composition possess different R.I.s. This has proved to be of great value in the identification of gemstones.

*Example:* There is no known natural, singly refractive, transparent gemstone with a R.I. between 1.50 and 1.70, so that any transparent stone found to be singly refractive on the polariscope and then found to have a R.I. between 1.50 and 1.70 on the refractometer may be identified as glass, as it is the only material to possess both these properties.

Instruments have been specially designed to obtain the R.I. of cut gemstones. These are called ''refractometers'' and are a vital and most efficient aid towards gemstone identification.

## CHOOSING A REFRACTOMETER

There are several types of refractometer in use at the present time. For many years the Rayner instrument, with an inbuilt index scale giving readings between 1.30 and 1.81, has been in general use.

This refractometer is now out of production, but there are so many about that it may be possible to get hold of one.

The Rayner Dialdex refractometer, which many gemmologists find easier to use than the one on the previous page.

12

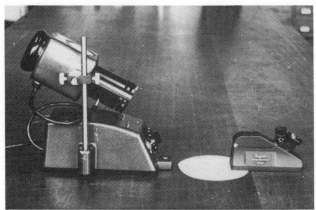

The refractometer must be used with light directed into the end and with the eye close to the eyepiece.

Only a small drop of R.I. liquid should be placed by the dropper on the glass table of the instument.

The replacement instrument now produced by Messrs Rayner is sold under the trade name Dialdex.

It has almost the same restrictions of R.I. reading, i.e. 1.40 to 1.81, but is an improvement over its predecessor in that the glass table, which is an essential part of its optics, is much more durable, and the wider spaced scale allows for more accurate readings to be obtained.

Various other refractometers with specialist refinements are available. One type produces a restricted range of readings, but the resultant wider gaps between one value and the next allow extremely accurate readings to be obtained. Others provide for higher R.I. readings to be available than is possible with the standard refractometers. These special refractometers are not often required.

## ON OBTAINING A READING

The refractometer should be set up, as illustrated, in front of a bright white light source.

If the eye is now brought to the eyepiece the index or screen of the instrument should be clearly seen and be brightly illuminated.

The refractometer will be provided with a bottle of R.I. liquid. Before any stone is placed on to the small glass surface which is embedded in the table of the instrument it is essential that a drop of this liquid is placed on to its centre. There should be sufficient liquid so that when the stone to be tested is placed on top of it the liquid will flatten out and cover the glass surface but not spill over it; a small stone will usually require only a small drop of liquid and a larger stone a larger drop.

If the scale of the refractometer is viewed through the eyepiece again at this point, a faint shadow edge should be seen near the bottom of the scale at about 1.81. This shadow edge is caused by the liquid, which has a refractive index of

1.81, and the gemmologist can look with satisfaction upon the fact that he has taken his first R.I reading.

The stone to be tested, which must have a fairly large flat polished surface (e.g. the table facet of a cut gemstone), should then be carefully placed onto the drop of liquid and into contact with the refractometer glass, so that it ends up with only a thin film of R.I. liquid between it and the glass.

Great care must be taken when carrying out this procedure, especially when using the Rayner refractometer, as the glass table of the instrument is extremely soft and can be very easily damaged. Small stones must be placed on with the use of stone tongs and when set stones are being tested extreme care must be employed as the extra weight of the metal setting can cause the stone to grind into the glass, leaving a scratch mark which will result in very poor R.I. readings being obtained subsequently. The instrument will then have to be sent away for expensive and time consuming restoration if clear readings are to be obtained.

When the stone is suitably placed on the refractometer the lid of the instrument may be closed over it. (This is not always possible with large stones or set ones, and is not absolutely essential). If the eye is now brought once more to the eyepiece, a shadow may be seen to cover part of the scale and the R.I. reading may be taken at the point where this shadow ends.

Where white light is used with the Rayner instrument, the shadow may have a coloured termination and the R.I. reading is taken at the lower edge of the green, where the green and yellow meet.

It is often necessary, when identifying a gemstone, to obtain the R.I. to the third decimal place. For this purpose, the gemmologist must learn to judge the position of the shadow edge in relationship to the degrees of the scale. If the edge comes half way between 1.61 and 1.62 then the R.I. will be 1.615; if slightly above, it will then be 1.616. If the shadow terminates almost at 1.62, then the reading will be 1.619, and so on.

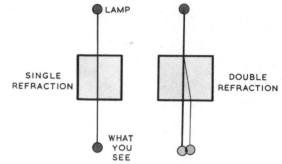

The principle of single refraction (left) and double refraction (right). If double refraction is strong, two images can be seen through the mineral.

The spot of R.I. liquid on the glass table of the refractometer should be as small as possible consistent with the size of the stone.

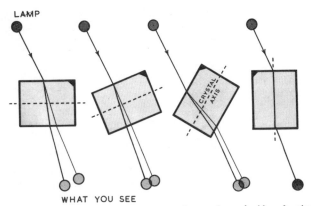

CRYSTAL AXIS

WHAT YOU SEE

Double refraction varies from none to a maximum when a doubly-refracting mineral is rotated. It is therefore important to check R.I. on more than one facet of a stone.

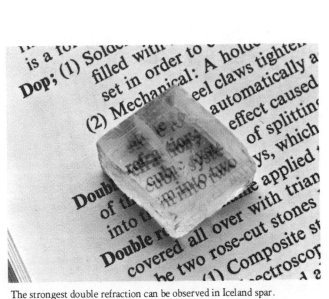

The strongest double refraction can be observed in Iceland spar.

# DOUBLE REFRACTION

Many gemstones are doubly refractive to light. Light entering the stone is split into two separate rays, each with its own refractive index. Thus two separate R.I. readings (i.e. two shadows) will appear on the refractometer. To obtain an accurate reading for each ray, a polaroid filter may be placed over the eyepiece. This filter only allows one of the rays at a time to pass through it, so that if the filter is rotated, the shadow edge relating to one ray and then the edge referring to the other will be seen.

To complicate matters a little further, it will be found that one, or both, of the rays has a refractive index which varies with direction, so that simply placing the stone on the refractometer and taking two readings is not enough to obtain the correct R.I.

The best method for obtaining the R.I. of doubly refractive stones is to look through the filter and watch the shadow edge of the ray with the filter in a static position. Rotate the stone a little at a time on its table facet, watching through the eyepiece to see if the shadow edge moves. Note the highest and lowest readings obtainable. Then give the filter about a quarter of a turn until the other ray is seen. Carry out the same procedure with this ray. Thus, the highest and the lowest possible R.I. readings of each ray are obtained and the extreme readings of these constitute the refractive index.

The difference between these two gives the birefringence (i.e. amount of double refraction) of the stone.

It will be found that one of the rays in some doubly refractive stones (for example tourmaline, amethyst, citrine, ruby, sapphire, emerald and aquamarine) will give the same R.I. reading no matter what the orientation of the stone, in which case that single reading may be noted as the refractive index of that ray, and the maximum or minimum R.I. of the other ray (whichever is furthest away) taken to complete the

R.I. of the stone. The birefringence of the stone may then be found by subtracting one R.I. reading from the other.

## DISTANT VISION TECHNIQUE

It has been found possible to obtain the refractive index of stones with domed or curved surfaces in an approximate way by employing a technique called ''distant vision''.

A small drop of R.I. liquid should be placed on the glass table of the refractometer and the stone carefully placed so that one part of the dome comes into contact with the centre of the glass. As this technique provides perhaps the easiest way of all to ruin the glass of the refractometer, the stone should never be scraped along the surface of the glass but *placed* in position.

If the eye is held twelve to eighteen inches away from the eyepiece, a reflection of the drop of liquid may be seen as a bubble on the glass lens of the eyepiece.

To assess the R.I. of the specimen the gem tester should move his head up and down a little at a time (not nearer and further away from the eyepiece but so that first the lower and then the higher parts of the refractometer scale are brought alternatively into view) until a shadow is seen to move across this reflected bubble. The R.I. may be judged at the position on the scale where the shadow cuts the bubble in half. Examples are shown in the diagram.

It should be noted that only one shadow edge will be seen, even with doubly refractive stones, so that it is not possible to assess birefringence in a stone accurately. The author has sometimes found it possible to obtain an approximate idea of the amount of birefringence however, by noting the varying position of the shadow edge when the stone is placed in different orientations.

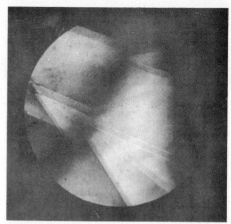

In zircon, double refraction is strong. The back edges of the stone appear to be doubled when viewed through the table with a lens.

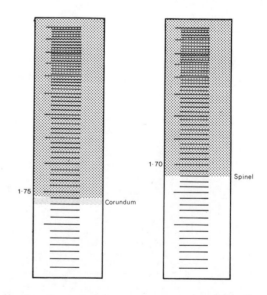

(Right) Reading of a singly refractive stone, spinel. (Left) Reading of a doubly refractive stone, sapphire.

16

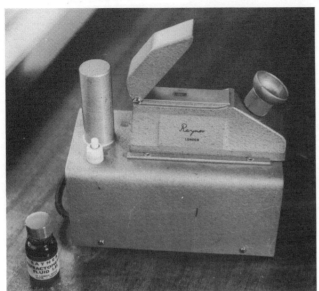

The sodium light source on which the refractometer stands provides a source of monocromatic light which provides sharper shadow edges.

## THE SODIUM LIGHT SOURCE

It is possible to use either of these types of refractometer with a reasonable degree of satisfaction with artificial white light, the Dialdex more so than the Rayner, but to obtain a high degree of accuracy with the instruments a sodium light source is necessary.

The sodium light source is designed so that the refractometer may be placed firmly in position in front of a beam of yellow light, with the result that a fainter, but very sharp, shadow edge is produced on the refractometer scale. Double refraction is much easier to see and to read using a sodium light source.

It is important to note that the upper limit of the refractometer's range is restricted to 1.81 by the R.I. liquid, so that a stone with a higher R.I. than 1.81 will put the scale in complete shadow. The stone is therefore unidentifiable with the refractometer. Notable examples are diamonds, zircons, and some garnets.

Sometimes a stone will give only an indistinct reading on the refractometer in which case perhaps only the edge (i.e. colour fringe when using white light) will be seen and the actual shadow be almost non-existent. This frequently happens with stones having an R.I. above 1.70. The reader should be on his guard against this. Should a stone appear not to provide a shadow, the whole of the scale should be examined very carefully.

It should also be noted that some glass imitation stones, although singly refractive, give slightly different R.I. readings when the stone is rotated a little. This is not to be confused with double refraction and should be ignored. (The stone will, of course, already have been proved singly refractive on the polariscope).

The R.I. liquid should not be left on the glass of the refractometer after use. The glass and the stone should be carefully cleaned after testing. Furthermore, it is advisable that the drop of liquid be replaced with a fresh drop after each test, as it has a tendency to solidify. During a spell of cold weather it may be found that the R.I. liquid has indeed become solid, in which case gentle warmth from an electric light bulb will cause it to become usable after five minutes or so. Some refractometer users always put a thin film of vaseline (petroleum jelly) on the refractometer glass table when the instrument is put away for any length of time, which protects it from the corrosive action of any traces of refractive liquid.

# THE MICROSCOPE

In the identification of gemstones, the situation is often reached when the stone has been proved to be the member of a certain gem species (i.e. ruby, sapphire, emerald etc.), with the use of the polariscope and refractometer, and all that remains to be ascertained is whether the stone is of natural origin or is a synthetic. A synthetic stone is the same as a natural one except that it is made by man, so that its composition and physical features are the same as the natural stone. (A stone employed to look like another, but not of the same material, is called an ''imitation'' or ''simulant''.)

In the majority of cases, the most satisfactory and in some instances the only method of doing this is by close examination of the internal features of the gemstone.

There are occasions when the 10x lens has sufficient magnification to enable this work to be carried out successfully, but in the majority of cases it is necessary to subject the stone to microscopic analysis.

The production of synthetic stones, in particular ruby, sapphire, emerald and spinel, is carried out on a large scale, and the R.I. of the majority of them is identical with that of their natural counterparts. The importance of the microscope in modern gem testing is therefore very evident.

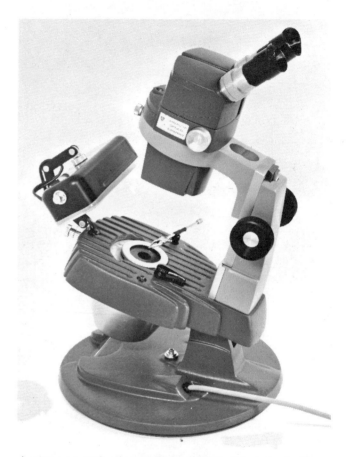

A microscope produced especially for gemmological use by the Gemological Institute of America called the Gemolite. It is binocular, has a zoom lens for different magnifications, and built-in dark field illumination to avoid the necessity for immersing gems in a refractive liquid when examining inclusions.

18

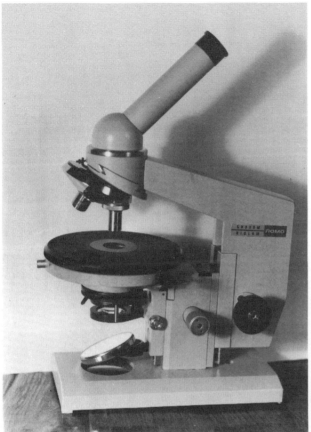

A low-priced Russian microscope which is suitable for gemmological work if a lower powered objective lens is fitted to the lens turret. It does not have dark field illumination and is used in conjunction with an intensity lamp.

Before obtaining a microscope, the reader would do well to study closely the following brief description of the construction of the instrument, during which reference is made to certain special requirements necessary for gem testing work.

The essential parts of the microscope are the tube (called the body tube) of the instrument and the two sets of lens which fit into the upper and lower ends of the body tube.

## THE EYEPIECE

Into the top of the body tube, a lens called the ''eyepiece'' may be fitted. This lens will either screw or slide into position. Microscopes are sometimes provided with two, three or more eyepieces of different magnification so that they may be interchanged.

## THE OBJECTIVE LENS

At the bottom of the body tube will be found either a single ''nose'', into which may be fitted any one of a number of lenses called ''objective lenses'', or a revolvable turret which carries two, three or four lenses, so that any one of them may be brought into use.

The total magnification of the eyepiece and objective lens in combination may be found by multiplying the power of one by the power of the other i.e. a 6x objective in combination with a 5x eyepiece will provide a magnification of 30x.

A microscope suitable for gemmological use will be one that magnifies an object by between 20 and 200 times. The instruments on the market which provide magnifications of between 100x, 200x or more and 800x to 1000x, are of little use to the gemmologist because the field of vision is far too small. They allow only a tiny fraction of the stone to be seen at any one time, whereas an overall picture is often required. The depth of focus also will be too shallow, which means that it is more difficult to search the stone internally for inclusions.

A sophisticated gemmological microscope by System-Eickhorst of West Germany which has dark field illumination in the form of a fluorescent ring light (bottom right). It is binocular and has a zoom lens. The microscope can also be used for examination by transmitted light by inserting the binocular lens unit into the clamp on the instrument shown on the left. The stone is held in a transparent cell holding RI liquid and illuminated by built-in intensity lamp, the binocular unit being horizontal.

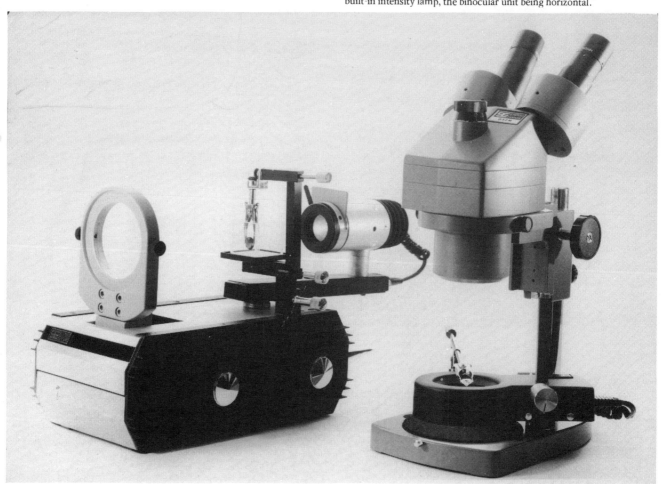

# THE STAGE

Directly underneath the body tube will be a round stage with a hole in the centre. The articles for examination are placed on this stage, generally on a glass slide or cell, and light directed through the hole from underneath so that the object is brightly illuminated.

# THE SUBSTAGE

Underneath the stage should be a number of useful accessories, together called the substage, which may include:—

(a) A diaphragm, which is similar to a camera diaphragm that can be opened or closed to restrict the beam of light through the stage to a chosen diameter. The beam can be adjusted to the complete width of the hole in the stage or down to only about a millimetre in width.

(b) A condenser, which is a glass lens for condensing the beam of light into an intense spot.

# PRODUCTION OF LIGHT

Beneath the substage will be either an inbuilt light source, or a pair of mirrors mounted back to back on a swivel platform so that either may be brought into use to reflect light up through the hole in the stage. One of the mirrors will be flat and is useful when daylight is the source, the other will be concave and of particular benefit with artificial light.

# DARK FIELD ILLUMINATION

Some microscopes are fitted with dark field illumination, which eliminates the need for immersion in a refractive liquid when studying inclusions. The background becomes dark and the inclusions brighter, the opposite effect from using transmitted light.

The stone is illuminated from the sides, either by a light in the substage mounted in a reflector with the central area blocked off to provide a ring of light (see illustration, right) or by a fluorescent ring light.

# FOCUSING ADJUSTMENT

The focusing of the microscope is carried out by adjusting the distance between the objective lens and the specimen by turning one of the focusing knobs, which will usually be located to the rear of the body tube. The largest knob is called the coarse adjustment and causes the body tube or the stage to move up or down relatively quickly. This is the focusing adjustment most commonly employed. There will be a smaller knob just below the coarse adjustment which causes the body tube to move only very slightly. It is intended for delicate focusing and is of particular use when higher magnifications are employed.

The correct method of obtaining focus is to rack the body tube down towards the specimen to be examined, watching its progress from the side, until the objective lens is quite close to the specimen, and then slowly raise the focus, with the eye looking through the eyepiece, until the specimen is brought into view. In this way it is impossible to damage the delicate glass of the objective by winding it down onto the hard gemstone. Many microscopes made today have a focal distance of two inches or thereabouts, so that this precaution is not so necessary.

The ring light for dark field illumination on the Eickhorst microscope can be used for mounted stones.

# EXAMINATION OF GEMSTONES

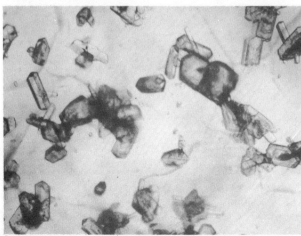

Inclusions in an aquamarine seen by dark field illumination.

Inclusions in a synthetic emerald seen by transmitted light.

There are several ways of setting up the stone for examination on the microscope and the most useful basic methods are now described. It is anticipated, of course that the reader will try all methods and will eventually find useful variations by trial and experiment.

1. The stone may be held in stone tongs as if preparing for examination with the 10x lens, and then positioned in the centre of the stage, the hand resting on the edge for stability. Set stones may be held or rested on the stage. The stone should then be brought into focus and maybe turned into any desired orientation. Inclusions inside the stone are often easily visible, but as with a 10x lens, it is beneficial in most cases to have either a thin piece of white paper or a piece of specially prepared ground glass underneath the stone. The light shining through will cause inclusions to stand out in relief against the white background.

2. The gemstone may be placed on a glass slide, held in the desired position by a piece of plasticine from one side, and then placed on the microscope stage for examination as before.

3. Useful little tongs may be obtained which fit into one of the holes usually provided around the outer edge of the stage, by which the stone, or its setting if it has one, may be held in any orientation over the stage aperture. Focus should be carried out as before.

4. The best method of examining inclusions in gemstones is by immersing the stone in a colourless liquid held in a clear glass cell. The aim of the liquid is to reduce the amount of light reflected from the surface of the gem,

therefore making it easier to see its internal features. Water is better than no liquid at all, but xylene, toluene, or a liquid of even higher refractive index is better. The stone under test should be completely immersed and focusing of the instrument carried out as before, being especially careful not to bathe the objective lens in the liquid.

Immersion of gemstones set in jewellery is not always practicable, particularly in liquids of higher R.I., as they are quite difficult to clean off, but can be used in some circumstances with a little ingenuity. Stones set in rings can often be examined from the rear, the whole setting being immersed face down in liquid.

When carrying out microscopic examination of a gemstone, it is generally best to make use of the lower power lenses in the first place, in order to obtain a general overall appearance of the stone, and to work slowly up to the higher magnifications in which a more detailed examination of particular parts of the stone may be carried out.

A gem held by plasticine on a glass slide for examination by microscope.

## THE SPECTROSCOPE

The purpose of the spectroscope is to analyse light which has been transmitted through, or is reflected from, gemstones. The instrument has an adjustable slit at one end, through which light from the gemstone may pass, and a small hole at the other end, by which analysis of this light may be viewed.

If the slit of the spectroscope is opened a little, by rotating the knob which protrudes from the side, and pointed at a source or ordinary white light, the result viewed through the eyepiece will be of all the colours of the spectrum. This is because white light consists of all these colours in combination and the spectroscope has the power to analyse, or break down, this light into all its components.

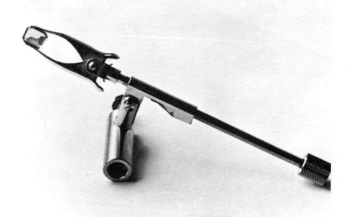

Special tongs for holding gems examined by microscope. The tongs fit into a hole on the microscope stage.

A modern hand-held Rayner spectroscope with a diaphragm of different sized slits.

A Beck hand-held spectroscope used on a special mount. The table holding the gem can be rotated. Light from an intensity lamp is directed on the gem.

When light which has passed through, or has been reflected from, certain gemstones is analysed by using a spectroscope, vertical dark bands or lines may be seen across the spectrum. These are called absorption bands, or absorption lines, and are the result of the stone's absorption of certain colours from white light. It has been found that the position and number of these is constant for gemstones with identical composition, and may thus be used as a means of identification. Occasionally bright lines are seen. These are emission bands.

The absorption bands and the colour of the spectrum may be considered by reference to a fixed scale of units called Angström units (abbreviated to A or AU) which are the units of measurement of the wavelength of light. The unit is equal to one ten-millionth part of a millimetre and the visible light scale reads 7000A at the red end, graduating to 4000A at the blue end.

The normal hand spectroscope is of the prism type and does not have this scale of reference built into it. A grating spectroscope with the inbuilt scale is available at greater cost. A scale is not really essential, however; descriptions of the absorption spectra of the gemstones refer to their approximate positions in relation to the colour bands in which they appear in the prism spectroscope, and also give the Angström units on which the bands centre.

The spectrum colours are compressed towards the red end in the prism instrument but are evenly spread in the grating one. It is normal procedure to view the spectrum with the red to the left, and it is best always to hold the instrument in this orientation. The identification of gemstones with the spectroscope depends more on familiarity with the absorption spectra of each substance than actual measurement of the position of the absorption bands. The effects look totally different ''upside down''.

In the USA, the spectra of gems are examined with the red on the right, so the diagrams in this book would have to be inverted.

# HOW TO USE THE SPECTROSCOPE

Generally, spectrum analysis of gemstones is best carried out on light which has been passed through them. There are a number of ways of doing this.

1. Set a white light source with an adjustable diaphragm so that it points directly upwards. Close the diaphragm until it allows the stone to rest safely over a small hole, which will then emit a powerful beam of light. The stone should be positioned so that the maximum strength of *COLOUR* is obtained, and then this light examined with the spectroscope.

If the light source has no diaphragm, a piece of metal large enough to rest over the end of the light source, with two or three holes of different size (say 2 mm, 4 mm and 6 mm), may be made quite simply and the stone placed over whichever of these holes is the correct size.

This method is satisfactory for loose and set gemstones, provided that the setting does not have a closed back, in which case the reflected light method must be used.

It may be worth pointing out that a considerable amount of heat is emitted by the light source and, when employing this technique, most of it tries to pass through the diaphragm, so that after a short while the stone can become very hot. Care should be taken to ensure that stones that are susceptible to heat (i.e. those that may crack or even change colour) are not left for too long a period at one time.

Also worth noting is that some stones seem to lose their absorption spectrum either totally or in part after being heated (a temporary loss fortunately) so this is another reason for submitting stones only to short spells on the light source.

The problem can be eliminated by using cold light transmitted through a fibre glass channel directed on to the stone, although this does restrict the amount of light (see illustration, right).

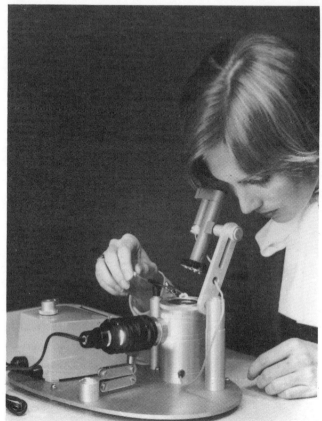

A spectroscope mounted on a special unit supplied by the Gemological Institute of America. The spectroscope has a scale and there is a built-in light source which does not heat the stone. When some stones are heated the spectrum can become less distinct.

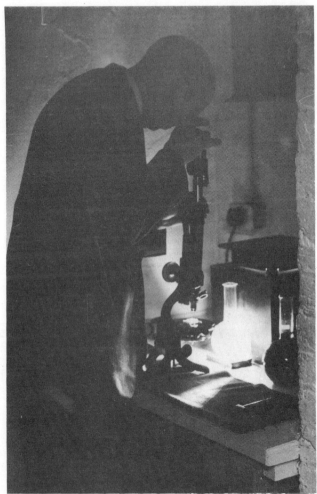

Using a spectroscope in conjunction with a microscope of which the eyepiece has been removed. The microscope acts as an intensity lamp. In this case a flask of copper sulphate coloured water is placed in front of the light in order to help visibility at the low end of the spectrum. The user, in this picture, is the famous pioneer of spectroscopy in gemmology, B. W. Anderson.

2. The stone may be placed on a clear glass slide over the aperture of the microscope stage and light transmitted through it as though preparing to examine its internal features (with the exception that all efforts should be made to cause the maximum amount of light to pass through the stone whereas this is not always desirable when examining inclusions). The eyepiece should be removed and the focus arranged so that the greatest amount of colour passes up the body tube, and then the spectroscope held over the tube so that the spectrum of the stone may be observed.

3. A bright white light source may be directed at an angle of about 45 degrees onto a piece of black felt, or similar material, and the stone placed table facet down on the material, in the brightest part of the light. If the stone is carefully positioned, light should enter one of the pavilion (back) facets, travel through to reflect from the inside of the table facet, and then come out of the stone from the pavilion facet on the opposite side. The light emitted may then be analysed with the spectroscope. This method can generally only be used with loose stones.

4. There are times when it is desirable to concentrate the attention on the blue end of the spectrum. Absorption lines are often more difficult to find here because the bright glow of the red colour ''blinds'' the eye. To overcome this problem a flask containing concentrated copper sulphate solution should be placed between the light source and the specimen, in which case all the red will be removed from the spectrum and the blue end be more easily examined. This method may be adopted with methods 2 and 3 but is not so practical with method 1.

The flask may be positioned so that it acts as a condenser. Adjusting the distance between it and the light source enables a concentrated spot of light to be ''focused'' onto the stone.

It is useful also to have available a flask of clear water, which, when used with method 3 acts as a coolant and condenser.

The spectroscope is an invaluable aid to gem testing, in particular for the quick and positive way zircon and red garnets may be identified, but a considerable amount of practice is essential before stones can be identified confidently.

## COLOUR FILTERS

The Chelsea colour filter is a little instrument which allows only the intense red and yellow-green parts of the colour spectrum to pass through it, the other colours being absorbed. This may be verified by examining light which has passed through the Chelsea filter with the spectroscope.

## METHOD OF USE

The stone to be tested should be illuminated with a bright white light source and examined against a white background, holding the filter close to the eye and a comfortable distance from the stone.

The instrument has little practical value used on its own but is useful in conjunction with other tests. Synthetic blue spinels, the majority of blue pastes and therefore garnet-topped doublets (composite stones consisting of a thin slice of garnet fused to a base of blue (or some other) coloured glass) will turn a fine red colour through the filter, whereas nearly all natural blue stones do not. The exception to this rule is a blue to violet-blue sapphire found in Ceylon which also turns reddish through the filter.

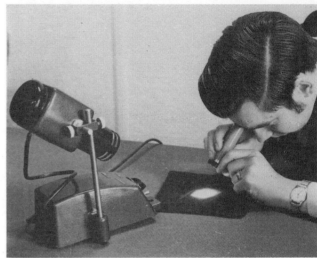

Using a spectroscope with a piece of dark black felt as background to the stone.

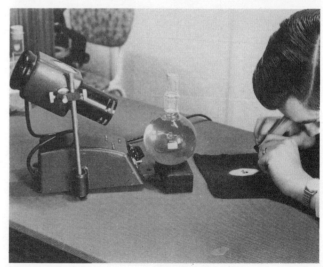

Using a spectroscope with the light passing through a flask containing concentrated copper sulphate solution so that only the green-blue in the lower end of the spectrum is passed, which helps in seeing lines at this end of the spectrum.

28

The Chelsea filter (devised at the original gemmological classes at Chelsea Polytechnic in London) which passes only red and yellow-green light.

The Chelsea filter is best used with white paper as a background.

If light is passed through copper sulphate solution on to a gem on black velvet, any colour seen through a Chelsea filter can be regarded as a fluorescent colour.

## COPPER SULPHATE SOLUTION

If a flask containing a concentrated solution of copper sulphate is prepared, it will act as a filter, absorbing the red, orange and yellow light and transmitting the green and blue only. Use distilled water and filter it to avoid milkiness.

## METHOD OF USE

The flask should be positioned in front of the light source in such a way that a bright blue condensed spot of light falls onto a piece of black felt-like material. The stone may be placed into this ray and examined as described in the section on spectrum analysis.

Alternatively, the stone may be examined through the Chelsea colour filter, when any colour seen may be considered to be fluorescence (explained in the following paragraphs). To obtain satisfactory results no other light source should be in the vicinity. This is called the crossed filter technique. Most rubies (including synthetic) and red spinels show up well by this method.

## ULTRA-VIOLET LIGHT

Certain gemstones, when placed under the invisible light rays called ultra-violet light, emit a visible glow. This effect is called fluorescence and in certain circumstances can prove to be of great diagnostic value.

There are two main types of ultra violet (u.v.) light source generally available and suitable for gem testing, the long wave (that which emits light between 3,000 and 4,000 Angströms) and short wave (that which emits light between 2,000 and 3,000 Angströms). It is necessary to have both types of u.v. light in the gem testing laboratory as in many cases it is the effects seen by a stone irradiated by first one and then the other source which prove to be of value, rather than the effects seen under just one radiation. A lamp with long and short wave u.v. is illustrated.

There are instruments on the market that contain both sources in one housing, and some that also incorporate a miniature dark-room. This arrangement seems to be quite satisfactory.

The use of the ultra-violet light source requires very little skill or practice. The stone needs simply to be placed under the source of radiation and its reaction noted. However certain precautionary words will not be amiss. Directly viewing the actual light source can cause permanent damage to the eyesight and should not be risked in any circumstances. Further, some gemstones, notably those which have a colour caused by heat treatment (such as zircons of the blue and colourless varieties), will be liable to alteration of colour to a detrimental extent if left under the radiations for more than a very short while.

Many diamonds and rubies along with red spinel, fluorspar, synthetic spinels, and sapphires, to name but a few, exhibit fluorescence, and in many cases this effect can prove diagnostic.

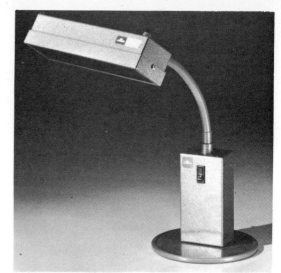

A bench type of ultra-violet lamp made by Allen of England.

## THE DICHROSCOPE

It was mentioned under the section concerned with the refractometer that light entering certain stones is split into two distinct rays. In many of the gemstones which possess this double refraction, each ray is of a different colour or is a different shade of the same colour. The effect seen by the eye is a combination of these two colours. The phenomenon is called "dichroism". Trichroism occurs when a stone

A portable ultra-violet lamp that can be switched to long (above) or short (below) wave light. It operates from a battery or the mains.

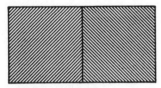

A dichroscope splits the light of a doubly-refracting stone into two images so that the colours of each ray can be compared.

exhibits three colours, although only two can be seen in any one direction and the all-embracing term is pleochroism.

There is an instrument which can separate the rays, so making it possible to see the different colours side by side. It is called the "dichroscope".

A gemmologist stranded on a desert island with nothing but a dichroscope and some stones to play with, would no doubt become quite resourceful and proficient in its use, but in the author's opinion, the instrument has very little gem testing value provided that other instruments are at hand.

Some pretty effects may be obtained and there are occasions when the presence of dichroism can be of confirmatory benefit, so that it is useful to have a dichroscope available.

While it is possible to buy a ready made instrument, it is far more economical to make your own. A rhomb of transparent calcite will be seen to double all that is viewed through it owing to its very high birefringence. It needs to be enclosed in a cardboard, wood, or metal tube which does not pass light other than lengthwise. One end is blocked off with the exception of a small central aperture. If the hole is then viewed from the open end it should be seen doubled.

## METHOD OF USE

The dichroscope is only of use with coloured stones. The stone to be tested should be well illuminated and its colour examined through the dichroscope from various directions. If the colour seen through the dichroscope is different in any way through both the holes seen at the same time, the stone is dichroic. The gemstone needs to be tested in different directions as there are certain directions in doubly refractive stones that do not show the effect.

Rubies show the effect quite well, one ray being a slightly paler shade of red than the other. Sapphire exhibits one

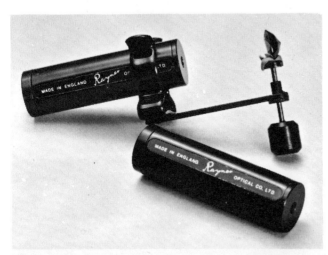

A dichroscope, an early gem-testing instrument that has limited use.

31

aperture light blue and the other medium to dark blue, and aquamarine shows one ray colourless and the other blue. Andalusite, alexandrite, and iolite, to name but a few, also show interesting effects through the dichroscope, as is mentioned in the section on actual identification.

## SPECIFIC GRAVITY

The specific gravity (S.G.) of a substance is its weight in comparison with the weight of an equal volume of water.

It was pointed out earlier that the refractive indices of gemstones are constants and therefore of practical use in their identification. The specific gravities of gemstones are also constants for each particular species and it follows that, if accurately measured, they may be used in a similar manner to R.I.s to assist in gem testing. Unfortunately the majority of stones that require testing are set in some form of jewellery, so that an S.G. test, which requires weighing the stone, is impractical.

There are times, however, when S.G. can come in useful. If, for example, the gemmologist is asked to identify the material from which a carving is made, then S.G. is practically the only method available.

## HYDROSTATIC METHOD

The essential information necessary to obtain the specific gravity by the hydrostatic method is as follows:—

a. The weight of the article.

b. The weight of the article while suspended fully immersed in water.

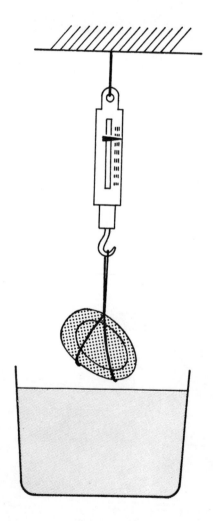

The specific gravity of a larger piece of mineral, such as a carving, can be measured by weighing it in air and then in water.

32

The weight of the equal volume of water may be calculated by subtracting *b* from *a*: call the result *c*. The final calculation is to divide *c* into *a*, the result being the S.G. of the material.

For largish carvings the weighings may be carried out with a spring scale, using a bucket of water and some string to weigh the piece immersed in water.

Smaller pieces require the use of more accurate scales, with pans and weights, using a container of water that can be held over one of the pans by some form of bridge, and fine wire, or cotton, with which to suspend the stone from one of the arms of the balance.

The Hanneman specific gravity balance, which will give a direct reading of the S.G. of a loose gem.

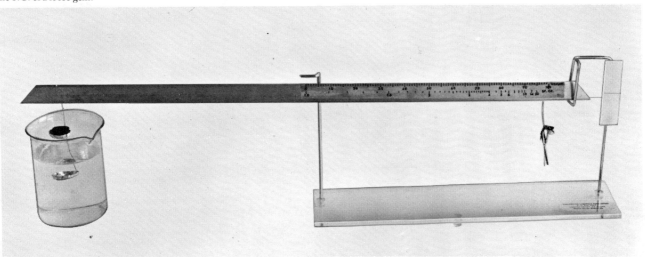

33

# THE HYDROSTATIC BALANCE

The easiest way of obtaining an accurate S.G. reading of a loose stone is to use the hydrostatic balance produced by Hanneman Lapidary Specialities, Castro Valley, California, USA. It is simply a long aluminium beam hung from the middle by a thread. The stone is weighed in air (in the upper cup, left, in the illustration), and the beam balanced by weights (right) until the needle at the end is on the scale line (right). Then the stone is transferred to the lower cup (left) and, because it weighs less in the water in the beaker, the beam is depressed at the opposite end.

Moving the weights inwards will bring the needle on to the line again, and the new position of the weights will give the S.G. to two places of decimals, read from the scale on the beam. The balance is useful for positive identification of stones such as diamond, with R.I.s too high to be checked on a refractometer.

## HEAVY LIQUID METHOD

If a stone sinks in a liquid, it has a greater S.G. than the liquid.

If the stone floats to the top of a liquid when placed with tongs some way beneath the surface, then the stone has a lower S.G. than the liquid.

If the stone remains suspended wherever it is placed in the liquid, neither rising nor falling, then it has an identical S.G. to that liquid.

## METHOD OF OPERATION

The normal practice is to have available liquids of known S.G. kept specially for the purpose of testing stones for specific gravity . They should be chosen by the individual to suit his own particular requirements. Useful liquids are:

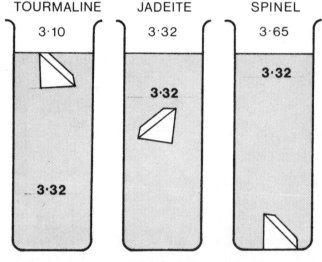

TOURMALINE 3·10    JADEITE 3·32    SPINEL 3·65

3·32

3·32

3·32

3·32

LIQUID—METHYLENE IODIDE

Principle of using a heavy liquid. Jadeite does vary in S.G. but when this is the same as methylene iodide, it will remain suspended in it. Otherwise it will rise slowly or sink slowly, if the S.G. is slightly below or above, when the stone is placed by tongs in the middle of the cell. A tourmaline will float and a spinel will sink.

Because a stone floats, this does not mean that it is a tourmaline. The actual S.G. is calculated by using other liquids, as explained in the text. Heavy liquids are probably more useful for eliminating certain possibilities than for establishing exactly what the stone is.

1. Bromoform diluted with monobromonapthalene to 2.65 (a piece of quartz may be used as an indicator that the S.G. is correct).

2. Bromoform diluted with monobromonapthalene to 2.71 (calcite can be the indicator).

3. Methylene iodide diluted with monobromonapthalene to 3.05 (green tourmaline as marker).

4. Methylene iodide pure S.G. 3.33 (no marker required).

The stone should be actually placed into the liquid, about half way down to the bottom, and then whilst viewing from the side, released and its reaction noted. A pretty shrewd idea of the S.G. can be assessed. If the stone sinks in a certain liquid, its rate of fall can indicate whether the S.G. of the stone is far higher than the liquid or not. It will sink quickly to the bottom if it has a much higher S.G., and it will sink slowly to the bottom if the S.G. is only a little higher.

Too much emphasis is not placed on S.G. tests here deliberately owing to the exceptional progress made in optical gem testing over recent years. Because of the problem of having to remove the stone from its setting this type of gem testing for mounted gems is rapidly becoming obsolete

## THE JEWELLER'S EYE

A gem-testing instrument depending upon a different principle from those previously employed is produced by the Hanneman company referred to on page 34. Called the "jeweller's eye", it measures electronically the reflectivity of the surface of a facet, normally the table facet, of a gem to give a direct reading of the gem on a scale. The instrument is sensitive to the cleanliness of the gem surface and to the

The Jeweller's Eye, an electronic instrument for helping to identify gems by comparing the reflectivity of their polished surfaces.

quality of its original polish, so false readings are possible.

Its main use probably lies in its employment as a comparator. For example, if a known YAG is tested on it and the needle adjusted to show YAG, then a suspected YAG should give the same reading. Neither this nor the hydrostatic balance is referred to in the testing procedures that follow, but if either is available it can be useful, particularly the balance, which may reduce testing time for loose stones.

## LOCATION OF THE INSTRUMENTS

Having obtained all the instruments required, a suitable place should be found for them to be permanently positioned. A bench or table with an electrical supply at hand, at which the gemmologist can sit with the instruments in front of him at a height that will make it possible to use them without having to stoop too low, is ideal for the purpose.

The exact relative location of each instrument on the table is not strictly important in gem testing, but a little thought can save a lot of time and a general guide may prove useful.

Place the main light source in a central position, about 18 inches back. In front of it may be placed the white or black materials used as background for gem testing, and the refractometer or copper sulphate solution.

To the immediate left, place the sodium light source, on which the refractometer may be left when not in use, and next to this the polariscope. These two instruments should be towards the front of the bench.

The microscope may be permanently positioned to the right of the light source so that it is possible to turn the light source only a little to direct it on to the mirror of the microscope, without having to move their basic positions. The other instruments may then be placed anywhere convenient. It will be seen that normal gem testing is carried out by starting on the left, moving slowly across to the right.

The author's laboratory set-up with instruments arranged for speed and convenience of use.

System-Eickhorst provide a modular unit in which various instruments can be incorporated. This one has, from the left, a cold light spectroscope with scale, an ultra-violet light chamber, a polariscope, and a refractometer.

# GENERAL GEM TESTING TECHNIQUE

A certain number of gemstones do not possess an appearance that is distinctive for any particular gem species. In such cases identification will have to be carried out without any preconceived idea of identity.

As with all things, the development of a technique, carrying out a series of tests in a logical order, will produce quicker and more accurate results than the haphazard wandering from one test to another.

The following sequence offers a broad basis for the development of such a technique.

*First test*

The gemstone should first be examined with the naked eye and under the magnification provided by a ten times lens, from all directions under a bright light source.

The surface of a stone rarely gives any definite indication of the stone's identity with the exception of diamond (fully covered under the relevant heading) and composite stones (i.e. imitation stones composed of two or more pieces of material, which may be either natural, man-made or one of each, fused or cemented together).

The latter stones may be identified by finding the join mark which separates the pieces, which may be seen either around or very close to the girdle of the stone, or around the facets between the girdle and table facet. It is easiest to see these marks when examining the stone with light from the source reflecting onto the stone and hence directly to the eye, using each facet as a mirror, or by immersing the stone in a liquid of fairly high refractive index. Even immersion in a white cup containing water will sometimes help.

The internal features of the stone under test, if it has been safely proved to be free of join marks, should now be examined for signs of bubbles, striae and curved growth

An ordinary cup with a white interior, filled with water, enables the sections of doublets and triplets to be made more visible.

Remember these singly-refracting (isotropic) gem-stones:—

DIAMOND
GARNET
SPINEL
FLUORSPAR
OPAL
AMBER
GLASS (PASTE)
STRONTIUM TITANATE*
YTTRIUM ALUMINATE*

* Synthetic materials imitating diamond. (Paste and synthetic colourless spinel are also used to imitate diamond).

lines, all typical of man-made stones, and for inclusions which might indicate a natural origin.

## Second test

The stone may now be tested on the polariscope to ascertain whether it is doubly refractive or singly refractive to light. This is a quick, easy and useful test. As its result eliminates many stones from the list of possibilities, it should not be overlooked.

A definite singly refractive result will narrow the field down to diamond, garnet, spinel, fluorspar, opal, amber, glass and a few lesser known materials, whereas a doubly refractive result will suggest that the stone is one of those listed in series B in the table of stones by refractive index at the end of the book, and those listed above may be ignored.

Should the test prove inconclusive, then the situation will have to be resolved during test three.

## Third test

The refractive index of the stone should now be obtained on the refractometer. If the stone has been proved to be singly refractive on the polariscope, only one shadow edge reading will need to be obtained and the table of stones by refractive index Section A should be referred to at the end of the book.

If the stone is doubly refractive, the refractive index of each ray must be obtained. Take care to see that both maximum and minimum readings for each ray, by testing the stone in different directions, are accurately taken. Refer to the R.I. table section B at the back of the book.

If the test on the polariscope was inconclusive then the possibility of the stone being doubly refractive will have to be carefully resolved on the refractometer by testing the stone in all directions whilst rotating the polaroid, making sure there is no movement of shadow edge whilst the polaroid rotates. Any movement will prove the stone to be doubly refractive.

Provided that the refractive index of the stone has been satisfactorily obtained, the species of the stone should now be known and the relevant section of the book may be turned to for complete identification. Should no reading be obtainable on the refractometer, it must be assumed that the stone has an R.I. above 1.81, the highest reading obtainable on the normal refractometer.

Spectroscopic analysis should be carried out, as there must be a strong possibility that the stone is either a zircon or garnet, each of which commonly possesses a distinctive spectrum.

### Fourth test

Once identification of the gem species to which a stone belongs has been carried out, it is often necessary — especially in the cases of sapphire, ruby and emerald — to ascertain whether the stone is of natural origin or is synthetic. In the majority of cases, the quickest and surest method of doing this is by examining the internal features of the stone with the microscope, the stone generally requiring to be immersed in a liquid of fairly high refractive index to obtain a clearer view of inclusions.

The four tests described form the basis of gem testing technique, but now we must consider when to use other instruments to advantage. A number of examples of gemmological problems may act as a useful guide.

### Example 1—Red Stones

It can often be time saving to use the spectroscope as an initial test when confronted with a red stone which has the appearance of being garnet. Even if it is proved not to be garnet, there are so many red stones with distinctive spectra that identity of species is quickly carried out. When faced with a large number of red stones for testing, a spectroscope will speed the time in which the stones may be sorted out into piles of garnets, rubies, spinels, red pastes, etc.

*Example 2—Blue Stones*

A quick and useful test which may be carried out with advantage on a large number of blue stones is examination of them all at once through the Chelsea colour filter. Make sure that a very bright light source is used. Stones that appear rich red under these conditions may be put to one side immediately and left to the end, when confirmatory tests need to be carried out to make sure they are all of man-made origin, and separated into synthetic spinels, pastes, and garnet-topped doublets. The possibility of some being natural spinel and natural sapphire must always be borne in mind, however.

*Example 3*

Suppose that normal gem testing methods have failed to provide either a refractive index or distinctive spectrum, it may be found useful to use the liquids available and obtain a rough idea of refractive index by immersion method. Remember the principle that the nearer the R.I. of stone is to the liquid it is immersed in, the more invisible it will become. The further away the R.I. from that of the liquid, the greater will be the degree of relief shown by the stone.

At least by testing the stone in all the liquids readily available, including the R.I. liquid (R.I. 1.81.), confirmation may be obtained that the stone has a refractive index above that of the refractometer and failure to obtain a reading was not due to other circumstances.

*Example 4*

Still considering the stone quoted in example three,

careful examination of the internal features of the stone can often provide enough evidence with which to identify a stone, although of course a thorough knowledge of the typical distinctive inclusions is necessary to make the test beneficial. The use of ultra-violet light often gives additional useful information.

To sum up, before admitting defeat and sending a stone to a gem testing laboratory, the gemmologist should repeatedly carry out all possible tests available in an attempt to identify the stone himself, as it is only by constant practice and by looking for things that do not appear to be there that improvement of gem testing ability can be achieved.


## WHERE TO BUY EQUIPMENT & STONES


The principal supplier of gemmological instruments in the United Kingdom is:

> Gem Instruments Ltd,
> St Dunstan's House,
> Carey Lane,
> London EC2V 8AB,

at the offices of the Gemmological Association of Great Britain and Northern Ireland. The firm also provides examples of all types of gem mineral, invaluable for practising on to improve technique and for using as comparison stones.

In the United States, similar services, on an even greater scale, are provided by:

> The Gem Instruments Corporation,
> 1660 Stewart Street,
> P.O. Box 2147,
> Santa Monica,
> California 90406.

This is in association with the Gemological Institute of America.

# Part 2

# IDENTIFICATION OF GEMSTONES

The second part of the book is devoted entirely to the identification of gemstones. The principle involved is quite simple:—

*1st*  Form an opinion, from visual observation, taking into account colour, transparency, lustre etc., as to the most likely identity of the stone.

*2nd*  Turn to the relevant section (the gemstones are treated in alphabetical order), and carry out the tests described until the stone is *proved* to be of that nature or *proved* otherwise.

*Example*

The stone under examination has the appearance of sapphire. Turn to the sapphire section and follow the instructions until a conclusive result is obtained.

Sometimes it may be difficult, or impossible, to carry out some of the tests satisfactorily, perhaps because the setting precludes the possibility of obtaining a refractometer reading, or a closed back setting makes spectrum analysis inconclusive. In such a case, reference may be made to the additional information provided on most stones in the hope that a further test, based on this information, may give positive identification.

There may be gemstones which do not bear resemblance to any particular well known gem species, and others which do bear such a resemblance but have been proved otherwise by the tests described. In such cases it is recommended that reference be made to the gem testing tables and advice at the end of this book, where a guide to the identification process in general is included.

# ALEXANDRITE

Alexandrite, a rare variety of the mineral chrysoberyl, appears green in natural light and red in artificial light.

*1st test* — Colour change.

The stone must be proved to possess this colour-change by viewing it in both types of light. Although it may be argued in some quarters that it is possible for a stone to be alexandrite and yet not possess colour-change, it is doubtful whether such a chrysoberyl would be accepted by stone dealers, jewellers or indeed the general public, as alexandrite.

*2nd test* — Polariscope: necessary result, double refraction.

*3rd test* — Refractometer.

The normal reading for alexandrite is 1.746 — 1.755 (0.009) but it is possible for the lowest ray to be 1.745 and the highest as high as 1.759, the birefringence being constant however at 0.009. If R.I. readings beyond these extremes are obtained, the stone should be viewed with the greatest mistrust. There is a synthetic corundum on the market that possesses a similar type of colour change to alexandrite and a R.I. of 1.76 — 1.77 (0.009). Natural sapphires have been found occasionally which also show a colour change, with the same readings. Careful observation will show that the shadow edges provided by alexandrite both move when the stone is turned on the glass table of the refractometer, whereas the upper shadow edge of sapphires remains static no matter what the orientation.

If the above tests have been carried out and satisfactory results obtained, the stone may be safely identified as alexandrite, but as there is now a synthetic alexandrite on the market a further test must be carried out before identification is complete.

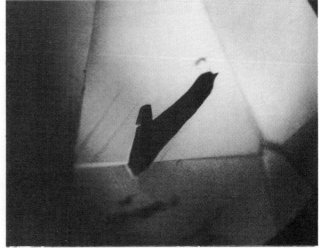

Synthetic ALEXANDRITE two phase inclusion

44

Synthetic ALEXANDRITE inclusions

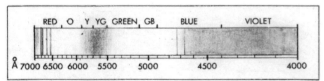

ALEXANDRITE spectrum

*4th test* — Microscopic examination of inclusions.

Under moderately low-power magnification, say 25x to 30x, natural alexandrite will be found to contain natural looking inclusions such as feathers and crystals, generally sparsely dispersed in an irregular manner.

Synthetic alexandrite will include the regular arrangement of twisted, veil-like feathers typical of so many synthetic stones.

*Other tests*

*Spectrum analysis*

The spectrum of alexandrite consists of a "doublet" of two strong narrow lines in the red (6805 & 6785 A), so close together that they appear as a single strong line, three weaker lines in the orange-red (6650, 6550 and 6450), and an absorption band covering the yellow and some of the green. The lower part of the blue and the violet are absorbed by a further band and it is often possible to pick out two fine lines just as this absorption band starts. The position and strength of the various bands and lines differs slightly depending on the direction down which the stone is viewed.

*Crossed filter test*

When examined between crossed filters, alexandrite will emit a red fluorescence. This characteristic is seen by some as being sufficient evidence to call a chrysoberyl stone alexandrite. A weak red fluorescence may also be seen when the stone is irradiated by either form of ultra-violet light.

*Dichroscope*

Analysis of the colour of the stone with the dichroscope will prove three colours to be present, green, purple and orange. Only two of these colours can be seen through the dichroscope at any one time, of course, and to see all three

45

the stone must be tested in different directions. The synthetic corundum imitations of alexandrite only produce two colours through the dichroscope no matter what orientation the stone is viewed.

# AMBER

Amber is the fossilised resin of pine trees. It may be found transparent, translucent, and virtually opaque, in colours varying from yellow to brown, reddish-brown or near white. It is light in weight, very soft, has a greasy surface appearance and is commonly used for making bead necklaces or for carvings and pendants.

The identification of amber poses some interesting problems and it is hoped that the following series of tests will go some way towards solving them.

*1st test* — Refractometer.

As before mentioned amber is a soft material so it should be quite simple to obtain the refractive index by distant vision without damaging the refractometer glass.

A reading of approximately 1.54 should be seen, a result which only goes as far as eliminating bakelite, a plastic (all synthetic resins will be referred to as plastics here for convenience) imitation which has a R.I. of 1.64 to 1.66, and possibly some glass imitations.

*2nd test* — Frictional electricity.

If amber is rubbed briskly against some soft material for a short time it will become electrified and be able to attract and pick up small pieces of paper. There are other similar substances that possess this power, so it is not a distinctive test by any stretch of the imagination, but the absence of frictional electricity will eliminate the possibility of a piece of ''amber'' being genuine.

AMBER Dead insects, as might be seen in amber or copal resin

46

*3rd test* — Internal examination.

Internal examination of the material under test with 10x lens and microscope will often be revealing.

a) Amber has been commonly found to include insects, moss, lichens and pine needles. Here again these are not always distinctive as the more recent fossil resin copal may also contain these inclusions. Further it has been known for insects to have been embedded in plastic imitations for good measure. Generally these insects are 'too good to be true' and will rarely fool the gemmologist, while test 4 will eliminate the possibility of copal resin.

b) Amber often contains bubbles, sometimes myriads of very tiny ones which cause the material to be cloudy in appearance, and at other times occasional larger ones. In any case these bubbles are nearly always spherical in shape. An imitation, called pressed amber, which is made by heating small pieces of genuine amber until soft and then pressing them through a sieve, causing them to amalgamate on the other side, also contains bubbles, but they are generally elongated in one direction. Some pressed amber may be made simply by pressing small pieces together under heat, after which margins between colour banded and clear areas are often seen in the finished product.

c) Some amber is "clarified" by heating in rape seed oil. The oil fills the bubbles which caused the cloudiness to make the amber more transparent and clear. This procedure often causes circular crack-like markings, called "sun spangles", to appear in the material. These can be very attractive and have been known to have been caused deliberately.

*4th test* — Ether test.

The possibility of the material under test being copal resin may be eliminated by placing a small drop of ether on the surface. When removed after a few seconds it will leave no impression on amber but leave a sticky mark on copal.

Another example of organic inclusions in AMBER

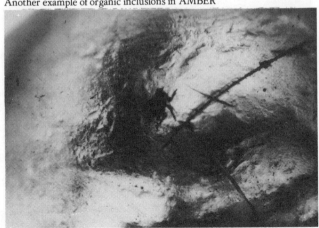

*5th test* —Fluorescence.

Amber may exhibit a bluish white fluorescence under long-wave ultra-violet light and a rather dim greenish effect under short-wave or a whitish fluorescence under both.

Copal resin fluoresces with a rather whiter effect. The plastics show either white fluorescence or may be virtually inert.

*6th test* —Specific gravity.

Where practical, the specific gravity measurement can be a very useful test.

If a solution is made up of ten level teaspoons full of salt in a tumbler full of water, amber and copal will be found to float whereas all the plastics will sink. This method is of course only practical with loose material or perhaps on a string of beads, which may be bound up into a ball and tested, ignoring the cord. The S.G. of amber is generally below 1.10 whereas all the plastics are well over 1.20.

*7th test* —Hardness, sectility and odour

As hardness, sectility and aroma produce such positive results, and as they are interesting characteristics of the material under discussion, details are now given and the reader left to his own discretion as to whether the piece under test warrants being damaged in the furtherance of identification, should further tests be required, of course.

Using a sharp knife it is a simple matter to cut into amber, copal resin and most of the plastics (bakelite offers most resistance but has already been eliminated in the first test) whereas glass will resist.

If an attempt is made to take a small peeling from the substance with the knife, natural and pressed amber and copal resin break away in small grains like crumbling pastry whereas the plastics come away in shavings.

If the pieces removed by the knife are then admitted to a flame and set fire to, the ambers and copal resin emit a pleasant aroma, while the plastics either have no smell at all

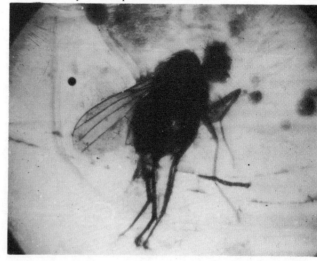

AMBER This fly has been preserved almost intact

48

or give off an unpleasant, even foul stink.

It is to be hoped that these tests will be avoided on good pieces of material.

*8th test*

The pressed amber mentioned above may often be identified by its distinctive effect when tested on the polariscope. True amber normally exhibits an anomalous doubly refractive effect, which will permeate the whole stone. Pressed amber shows the same effect but in little patches, repeatedly, throughout the material. This is due to the material being composed of many pieces of material, each individual piece showing its own anomalous effect when the whole is tested.

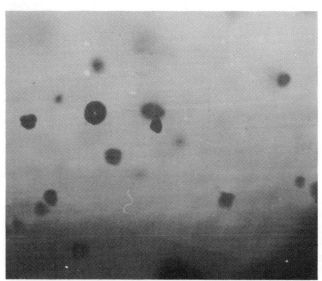

AMBER  Heavy, irregular, treacly bubbles are seen here

Spangled AMBER

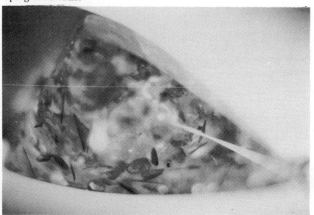

# AMETHYST

The identification of amethyst, the purple or violet member of the quartz family, is a relatively easy task. The stones are generally transparent, though the presence of many inclusions can render them virtually opaque, and the colour can range from a hardly perceptible tint through to an intense, magnificently rich purple.

*1st test* — Polariscope: Necessary result: double refraction.

*2nd test* — Refractometer.

The refractive index of amethyst is 1.544 — 1.553 (0.009) and is constant. The lower shadow edge remains static no matter what the orientation of the stone and the higher edge either moves, or in some cases, remains static, when the stone is rotated. This depends upon the cut of the stone.

Satisfactory results from these two tests confirm the stone as amethyst.

*Other tests*

The inclusions found in amethyst are interesting and often diagnostic.

AMETHYST A common and quite distinctive inclusion is a peculiar feather which has been called 'tiger-stripe'

AMETHYST This example is much more dramatic

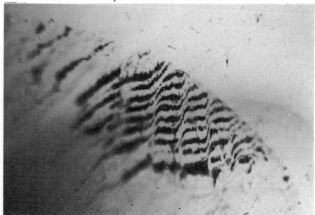

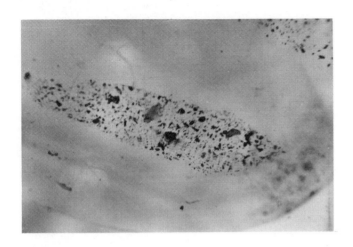

ABOVE LEFT
AMETHYST Another common feature is the inclusion of many irregular pieces of 'muck'; a good description of the interior of many amethysts

ABOVE RIGHT
AMETHYST Colour-zoning, showing distinctive and often angular margins is another common feature

LEFT
AMETHYST A definite angular demarcation line runs up the stone near the centre. The effect is not determinative as the author has seen an identical effect in a glass imitation

51

# ANDALUSITE

This unusual gemstone is occasionally found with a rich green coloration, but more commonly a brownish-green body colour with occasional flashes of red.

*1st test* — Polariscope. Necessary result: double refraction.

*2nd test* —Refractive index.

A refractive index reading approximating to 1.64 should be obtained, with a birefringence of 0.009 or 0.010. Extreme readings of 1.634 and 1.648 may be encountered but the double refraction will not normally exceed 0.011, so that confusion with tourmaline, which has a similar R.I. but a birefringence not less than 0.014, will be unlikely. Both shadow edges will normally move when the stone is turned on the refractometer, another fact to separate it from tourmaline because the higher shadow edge in tourmaline is always static.

Satisfactory tests on polariscope and refractometer are all that is necessary to prove the stone to be andalusite.

*Other tests*

*Dichroscope*

On examination of the colour of the stone with the dichroscope it is normally possible, by testing in different directions, to find three colours, yellow, green and red, the latter colour often of extraordinary intensity.

*Spectroscope*

The deep green andalusite has an absorption band in the green (5525A) which has a sharp cut off on the blue side but which gradually dissipates into the yellow. Fine lines may be seen in the green and towards the blue and in the blue to violet area a strong band may be seen, partially masked by the general absorption in that area.

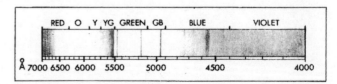

Green ANDALUSITE spectrum

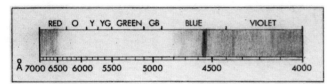

Paler ANDALUSITE spectrum

In the stones which do not possess such a rich green coloration, the band in the blue-violet is the strongest, and is accompanied by a narrow one a little further into the violet. The use of the copper sulphate filter may help in viewing these bands in the violet end of the spectrum.

## APATITE

Apatite has been found, and occasionally set in jewellery, in pleasant shades of yellow, blue, violet and green, but the softness of the stone precludes its being used to any great extent.

*1st test* — Polariscope. Necessary result: double refraction.

*2nd test* — Refractometer.
R.I. readings between 1.63 and 1.64 should be obtained with very small birefringence, between 0.002 and 0.004. Both shadow edges move on rotation of the stone but with such a small birefringence it is not easy to follow this effect.

The inexperienced gemmologist may not be too happy at identifying the stone by this birefringence alone, particularly bearing in mind that topaz, tourmaline and danburite have R.I.s in the same vicinity.

*3rd test* — Spectroscope.
Yellow and green apatite show an interesting spectrum, due to a rare earth element called didymium, which consists of a group of fine lines close together in the yellow, and a similar but weaker group in the green. There are two fairly strong narrow bands in the blue. It should be noted that danburite also possesses this didymium spectrum, but only very much more weakly.

The blue stones also show a spectrum, with two fairly strong bands in the blue and fine lines in the orange. Both effects described are best seen using the narrowest slit possible on the spectroscope.

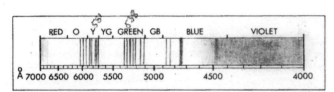

APATITE spectrum

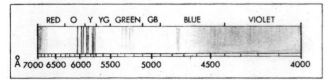

Weaker APATITE spectrum

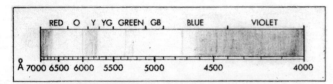

Very weak APATITE spectrum

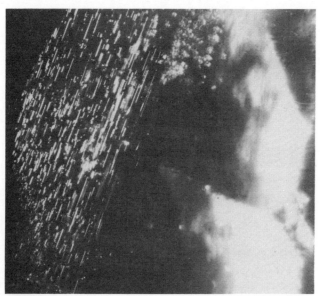

AQUAMARINE 'Rain' inclusion consists of a series of short, needle-like fragments all pointing one way in a group. Seen by dark-field illumination, the inclusions are lit from above against a dark background

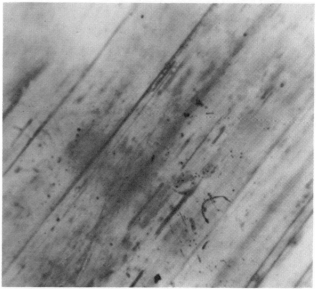

AQUAMARINE Similar effect, but with longer needles, seen under normal lighting

AQUAMARINE 'Cherry' inclusions are spheres often seen with stalk-like appendages

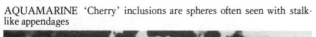

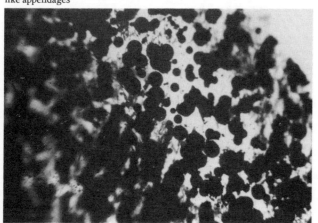

AQUAMARINE Two-phase inclusions are found in many stones

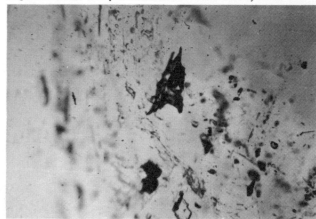

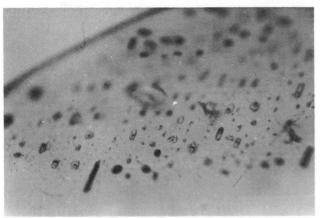

AQUAMARINE Two-phase inclusions are cavities containing a gas bubble and liquid. Generally elongated, they run in series with the long sides parallel

AQUAMARINE Two-phase inclusions often are long and canal-like with occasionally jagged outlines

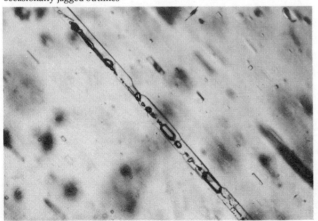

*Dichroscope*

Blue apatite exhibits strong dichroism, one ray being blue, the other pale yellow.

The other varieties of apatite generally show dichroism, but only weakly.

# AQUAMARINE

Aquamarine is the pale to rich blue or green-blue member of the beryl species of gemstones.

*1st test* — Polariscope. Necessary result: double refraction.

*2nd test* — Refractometer.

The refractive index of aquamarine approximates to 1.58 with a birefringence of 0.006 or sometimes a little more. There is no doubly refractive transparent gemstone other than aquamarine with anything like this R.I. so the test, if satisfactorily carried out, is conclusive.

*Other tests*

*Dichroscope*

Even when quite pale, aquamarine shows relatively strong dichroism. One ray is colourless and the other blue.

*Microscope*

Aquamarines generally look completely clear when examined with the naked eye. When the stones are immersed and examined with the microscope, however, they are often found to have distinctive inclusions.

# CAT'S-EYES

Some gemstones have numerous needle-like crystals of some other mineral growing through them. If there are enough of these inclusions running in one direction and the host material is cut as a cabochon (domed) in the correct orientation the resulting stone may show a cat's-eye effect, i.e. if a single light source is held over the stone a band of reflective light is seen, which in the better examples moves across the stone when it is tilted from side to side.

The most satisfactory method of identification of cat's-eyes is to obtain the refractive index, using the distant vision technique.

This list of possible cat's-eyes, with R.I., and other means of identification where thought necessary, should prove helpful.

CHRYSOBERYL CAT'S-EYE

| Refractive index | Stone | Other tests and description |
|---|---|---|
| 1.54 to 1.55 | *Scapolite* | Pink, blue, or violet (normally translucent). Dichroscope: pink and violet stones show two colours. Spectroscope: pink and violet stones show lines in the red of the spectrum and a broad band in the blue. Long wave U/V light: yellow or orange fluorescence. Short wave U/V light: slight pinkish fluorescence. |

| | | |
|---|---|---|
| 1.55 approx | *Quartz* | Yellow-brown, golden-brown, dark blue, red-brown. Often artificially coloured green, red, violet, etc. Often exhibits more than one band of reflective light. |
| 1.57 | *Emerald* | Green. Rare. |
| 1.60 to 1.62 | *Tremolite* (Amphibole) | Green |
| 1.62 to 1.65 | *Tourmaline* | Generally green, other colours possible. The separation of tourmaline from tremolite could cause problems but with tourmalines it is generally possible, by testing the stone in different directions on the refractometer, to obtain a degree of double refraction, which will take the R.I. to about 1.64, too high for tremolite. |
| 1.64 | *Apatite* | Greenish, yellowish, translucent, generally weak cat's eye. Yellow stones exhibit didymium spectrum (see under apatite). |
| 1.67 | *Enstatite* | Dark green or brown, opaque. |
| 1.69 | *Diopside* | Green or black. |
| 1.75 | *Chrysoberyl* | Honey-yellow, greenish-yellow, brownish-yellow. |

See also under star stones.

# CHALCEDONIES

Chalcedony is the name applied to a number of gemstones of varied appearance which are all members of the quartz species but which are cryptocrystalline (i.e. the material is made up of countless numbers of crystals which are so small they could not be seen even with the use of the microscope).

The main varieties under their nicknames are:

| | |
|---|---|
| Chalcedony | white, translucent, often with delicate banding. |
| Jasper | orange-red to brown-red, opaque. |
| Cornelian | orange-brown, translucent. |
| Onyx | black and white, banded. |
| Bloodstone | dark green with occasional speckles of blood-red. |
| Chrysoprase | bright grass-green, translucent. |
| Moss-agate | colourless, transparent, with inclusions which have a moss-like appearance. |

Most chalcedony can virtually be identified at sight. The mineral is so cheap that synthetics, or even imitations, are more expensive to produce than it costs to obtain the natural material, so making them an uncommercial proposition. The only real exception is chrysoprase, as its beautiful apple green colour and its relative rarity make imitation worth while.

Formal identification of chalcedony may be carried out as follows:

*1st test* — Polariscope: no double refraction is normally seen, or at the most only an anomalous effect.

*2nd test* — Refractometer.

A reading between 1.53 and 1.54 should be obtained, with either no birefringence or else a constant double refraction, no matter in what the direction the stone is tested, of up to 0.006.

CHRYSOPRASE spectrum

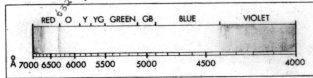

Green CHALCEDONY spectrum

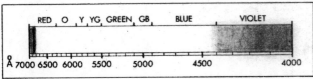

Stained green CHALCEDONY spectrum

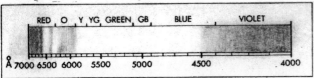

*3rd test* — Internal examination

Translucent stones may be examined with the 10x lens, a strong light source shining from underneath the stone, under which conditions it is normally possible to pick out the natural banding that most chalcedonies possess. Care needs to be taken, as some paste imitations show a similar effect owing to the colouring elements not being evenly distributed through the stone. Should doubt exist, further careful examination with the microscope would almost certainly result in bubbles being found if the stone were glass. Bubbles are a common inclusion in translucent pastes (glass).

Very special care needs to be adopted in the identification of chrysoprase as there are three different types of apple green chalcedony, and only one of them can truly be named chrysoprase.

*Confirmatory tests on apple green stones*

*Spectroscope*

True chrysoprase, coloured by the element nickel, shows a faint line in the lower region of the red (6320 A).

Green chalcedony, coloured by chromium, exhibits a strong doublet, a pair of lines very close together, high in the red.

Stained green chalcedony, which shows a rather fainter doublet in the red, has two weaker lines in the lower red area, which appear to have a bright patch at the side of each.

Moss agate may be imitated by applying silver-nitrate to chalcedony. The substance seems to eat its way into cracks and gives an effect similar to the real thing. Doublets are also sometimes made but it is doubtful whether either of these imitations would pass careful examination with the lens by even an inexperienced gemmologist.

# CHROME GROSSULAR GARNET

A fairly recent arrival on the commercial gem market, chrome coloured grossular garnets may be a rich dark green with a tourmaline appearance, grass-green similar to emeralds, through to a pale almost peridot-green.

*1st test* — Polariscope: single refraction, but most stones exhibit anomalous double refraction effect.

*2nd test* — Refractometer: between 1.74 and 1.75.

*3rd test* — Spectroscope.
   Typical chrome absorption spectrum of fine lines in the red and general absorption of the yellow-green.

*4th test* — Ultra-violet light.
   Red fluorescence may often be seen but only by reflection from the inside of the back facets of the stone. If the gem is placed table facet down a red reflective effect will be seen from the inside surface of the table facet. All stones of this type but one, tested by the author, have shown this effect, but it is not yet certain to be a reliable distinctive effect.

*5th test* — Microscope.
A number of distinctive inclusions have been noted.

CHROME GROSSULAR GARNET A typical internal feature is a series of irregular inclusions, many two-phase, all in the same plane but arranged in a curve

CHROME GROSSULAR GARNET These dark irregular inclusions with 'tails' have been nicknamed 'tadpoles' for obvious reasons

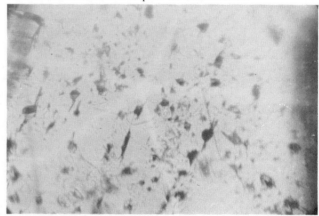

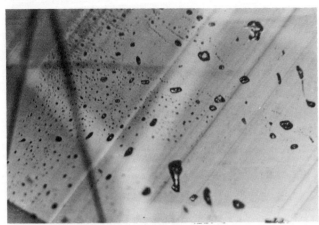
CHRYSOBERYL Two-phase inclusions are common and confirm the natural origin. They are not determinative to the species

# CHRYSOBERYL

Apart from the alexandrite and cat's-eye varieties of chrysoberyl, discussed under their relevant headings, the mineral also produces transparent stones of a yellow-green or yellow-brown colour.

*1st test* — Polariscope: Necessary result, double refraction.

*2nd test* — Refractometer.
An R.I. between 1.74 and 1.76 should be obtained with birefringence of 0.009. Average readings are 1.745 — 1.754. It will be found that both shadow edges move on rotation of the stone.

*Confirmatory test* — Spectrum analysis.
Analysis by spectroscope will show a strong band in the lower blue (4420A) and two fainter lines in the green-blue area (4860 and 5040A). The spectrum can generally be seen best when blue light from the copper sulphate solution is used to irradiate the stone.

*Other tests* — Microscopic analysis.

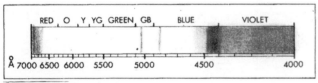
CHRYSOBERYL spectrum

# CITRINE

This yellow variety of the mineral quartz is often mis-called ''topaz''. The colour may vary from a pale straw-yellow to a rich golden colour and sherry-brown.

*1st test* — Polariscope, double refraction.

*2nd test* — Refractometer.

The R.I. of quartz is very constant at 1.545 — 1.554 (0.009). The lower shadow edge is always the same; the upper one moves. Sometimes the readings can be a little lower, but not more than 1.540, and the double refraction is always the same.

Natural citrine is quite a rare variety of quartz. Virtually all the material on the market is heat-treated amethyst. An indication as to whether the stone is natural or not can be obtained by use of the dichroscope, as natural citrine is quite strongly dichroic, whereas the heat-treated amethyst is not.

# CORAL

This is an organic material consisting of a conglomeration of skeletons left by tiny sea creatures called polyps. The colour generally ranges from pure white through various shades of pink to a fine rich pink-red.

*1st test* — Surface structure examination.
Using the lens, or possibly the microscope, with an overhead light, the surface will be seen to have a slightly irregular polish. Glass imitations will of course have a smooth polish. Delicate straight colour banding may normally be seen, which distinguishes coral from most of its imitations.

*2nd test* — Effervescence.
If a small drop of hydrochloric acid is placed on the surface of coral, it will effervesce quite briskly. This test should cause no damage to the coral provided that the acid is rubbed off quickly.

*3rd test* — Specific gravity.
Where practical, a hydrostatic S.G. test will prove conclusive with a result of about 2.68.

# DANBURITE

Danburite is found as transparent colourless, yellow and occasionally pink stones.

*1st test* — Polariscope: double refraction.

*2nd test* — Refractometer: 1.630 — 1.636 (0.006).
   Obviously great care is required when separating topaz from danburite on the refractometer alone as the birefringence only differs by 0.002.

*3rd test* — Fluorescence.
   Danburite may be separated from topaz by irradiation under ultra-violet light, where a light blue fluorescence should be seen under both long and short wavelengths. Topaz on the other hand generally emits a pale yellow or orange yellow glow.
   Where practical, danburite will be found to float on S.G. liquid 3.05, whereas topaz will sink.

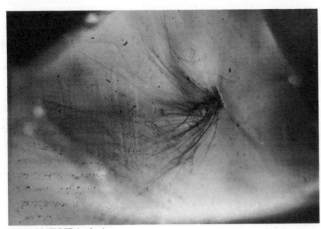

DEMANTOID inclusions

# DEMANTOID GARNET

The brilliant grass-green member of the garnet family called "demantoid" is now one of the rarest and costliest gemstones on the market. It may be identified by two methods, either of which is conclusive on its own.

*1st test* — Microscopic analysis
Examination of the internal features of the stone with the microscope will often be diagnostic as demantoids generally contain groups of radiating fibres often springing from a common point, which has been nicknamed a "horsetail" inclusion owing to its similarity to a horse's tail. Presence of such inclusions in a green stone will prove demantoid as being the identity of the stone without doubt.

*2nd test* — Spectroscopic examination
The spectrum of demantoid is equally distinctive. A strong band in the deep blue (4420A) may be seen which generally acts to cut off completely the lower end of the spectrum, and often fine lines may be seen in the red.

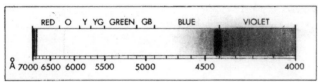

DEMANTOID spectrum

65

# DIAMOND

Diamond, the best known, hardest and, commercially, the most important of all gemstones, is the easiest to identify, owing to its distinctive appearance.

Most beginners have difficulty however, probably because there are no simple practical and positive tests normally available with the result that visual judgement has to be relied upon.

There is no easy way towards proficiency in diamond recognition. Regular handling of stones and careful examination of them being the only way, but in the initial stages the following tests may be found useful. The first section is devoted to tests based on certain attributes of diamonds and the second on identifying stones likely to be used to simulate them.

*1st test* —Examination of the stone in a good light with the unaided eye.

It is preferable to carry out all examination of diamonds in one location and under the same conditions. Fluorescent tubes should be avoided as a light source. A single tungsten light, perhaps fitted to an Anglepoise lamp, is the most convenient.

In the initial examination the stone should be held well away from the light source and the eyes, and looked at from various directions moving the stone about slowly. Under these circumstances, brilliant-cut diamonds will exhibit a continual "life", and there will always be evidence of the internal reflective ability of the stone.

The majority of the imitations when examined in a similar manner will mostly appear quite bright, but in certain directions will have a "dead" appearance.

As this examination is carried out the exceptional lustre of diamond will be noted also, as each facet of the stone acts as a little mirror.

DIAMOND Some stones have part of the original 'skin' on the girdle, a firm indication of their natural origin

DIAMOND A doublet removed from its mount: only the top is true diamond

The only way to gain proficiency in this initial test is to practice with known diamonds and diamond simulants. There is no short way to consistency. For the beginner it is a help if he or she can find someone to put together a sample group of diamonds and simulants as a little test.

*2nd test* — Examination with 10x lens.

The closer inspection provided by examination with a 10x lens is a simple continuation of the first test, but here the lustre and hardness of diamond will be even more apparent. If the stone is tilted at the correct angle, it should be possible to see a clear reflection of the light bulb on the table facet of the gemstone, as the facets of diamonds are perfectly flat and act as mirrors. No other gemstone will show a perfect mirror image of the light bulb in this way.

Next, the facet edges, i.e. the edges between adjoining facets, should be examined. Owing to the extreme hardness of diamond, these are always perfect in finish and appear to have a 'knife-edge' sharpness. Here again comparison with other gemstones will be necessary before proficiency is obtained, but it will be noted that some of the gemstones used to emulate diamond are, in comparison, extremely soft, and the rounded facet edges will give them away.

The following table shows the hardness of diamond and its simulants on Mohs' Scale, which simply indicates that one higher in the scale will scratch another lower in the scale. The positions are not proportional. In fact, the hardness of diamond is much greater to sapphire than sapphire is to talc. Stones with a hardness of 6 or less will most certainly show distinct rounding of the facet edges. To those with a hardness of more than 6, whose facet edges may not be quite so distinctly rounded, I have added a simple test for separating from diamond.

*Relative hardness of diamond and its simulants, showing simple tests that may be used for stones which are fairly hard*

| | | |
|---|---|---|
| Diamond | 10 | |
| Sapphire (natural and synthetic) | 9 | (Double refraction on polariscope) |
| Y.A.G. | 8 | (Virtually disappears in R.I. liquid 1.81) |
| Topaz | 8 | (Double refraction on polariscope) |
| Spinel | 8 | (R.I. on refractometer) |
| Zircon | 7½ | (Doubling of back facets) |
| Quartz | 7 | (Double refraction on polariscope) |
| Synthetic rutile | 6½ | (Doubling of back facets) |
| G.G.G. | 6 | |
| Strontium titanate | 5½ | |
| Lithium niobate | 5½ | |
| Scheelite (natural and synthetic) | 5 | |
| Paste (typical) | 5 | |
| Blende | 3½ | |

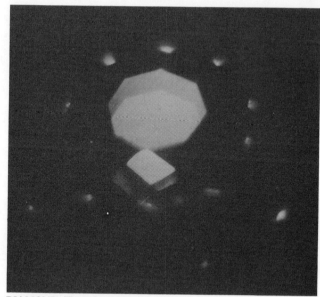

DIAMOND The reflections seen in the table of a doublet if it is slowly tilted away from the eye

Note: Y.A.G. is the synthetic material yttrium aluminate, often called ''Yag'' from yttrium aluminium garnet. G.G.G. is the synthetic material, gadolinium gallium garnet.

### Water drop test

Another useful little test which is related to hardness, the water drop test, is based on the principle that if a small drop of water is placed upon the clean, dry table facet of a gemstone, it will quickly spread out to cover more of the surface of a soft stone than a hard one. This can be proved simply by carrying out the test on a diamond and taking note how the drop of water, which should be placed on by means of a glass or metal rod, or dropper, does not spread out over the surface but stays rigidly in position for some time. If the test is carried out on softer stones it will be seen that the water spreads out more quickly in relative proportion to the softness of the stone.

Whilst carrying out examination with the lens, the possibility of diamond doublets must be considered. These stones, composed of a crown of real diamond on a base of a cheaper colourless substance, are extremely difficult to detect when set so that the girdle cannot be examined. The best way to identify them is to look into the stone through the table facet at an angle of 45°, where it will be possible to see the reflection of the table facet edges in the junction layer.

At this point it is worth noting that diamond has a refractive index of 2.418, so a reading on the refractometer will not be possible. Although it might be tempting to put a suspected diamond on the instrument to make sure there is no reading, it would be most unwise to do so as the stone is so hard that even when great care is used it is difficult to avoid damaging the soft glass of the instrument.

Diamond is a singly refractive substance, but most diamonds will give an anomalous effect similar to, but not as definite as, that given by doubly refractive stones, if tested on the polariscope sideways on. As it is the identification of set stones with which we are most concerned, it is not a very practical test as the stones are often so small and have so many facets that the presence or absence of double refraction is almost impossible to assess. However, for the inexperienced gemmologist it is worth trying the polariscope as he may have the surprise of seeing clear double refraction, in which case, of course, it is not possible that the stone is a diamond.

*3rd test* — Refractive liquids

If a stone is placed in a liquid of similar R.I. to its own, it will virtually disappear. If it is placed in liquids of differing R.I. it will stand out in relief and the greater the difference between the R.I. of the stone and the liquid the greater will be the relief exhibited by the stone.

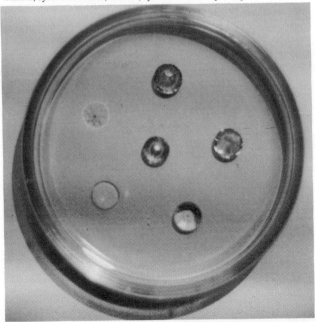

DIAMOND The refractive liquid test showing how the diamond in the centre compares with its imitators. Clockwise from the top: Strontium titanite, synthetic Rutile, Zircon, synthetic white Spinel, paste

If doubt exists following the first two tests, it can be beneficial to try immersing the stone in various liquids and noting the amount of relief with which the stone stands out.

It is necessary to use liquids of a known refractive index, and the further away the R.I. of the liquid from the R.I. of diamond, the greater should be the relief exhibited by the stone. Quite a useful liquid which is made use of in this way is that provided with the refractometer, which has an R.I. of 1.81. A table showing the R.I. of diamond, its simulants and the liquids available, is appended as well as simple tests to separate stones unlikely to be easily discriminated from diamond.

## REFRACTIVE INDEX TABLE

| | | |
|---|---|---|
| Synthetic rutile | 2.61—290 (.287) | (Doubling of back facets) |
| Diamond | 2.418 | |
| Strontium titanate | 2.41 | (Rounded facet edges) |
| Blende | 2.37 | (Rounded facet edges) |
| Lithium niobate | 2.21—2.30 (.090) | (Doubling of back facets) |
| Zircon | 1.926—1.985 (.059) | (Doubling of back facets) |
| Scheelite | 1.918—1.934 (.016) | (Fluorescence under short wave ultra-violet) |
| G.G.G. | 1.92 (approx.) | (Fluorescence under short wave ultra-violet) |
| Y.A.G. | 1.834 | (Virtually disappears in R.I. liquid) |
| R.I. liquid | 1.81 | |

Sapphire        1.76—1.77
  (natural and    (.008)
  synthetic)
Methylene
  iodide        1.74
Spinel          1.727
Monobromo-
  napathelene 1.66
Paste           1.635
                (Typical)
Topaz           1.61—1.62
                (0.010)
Bromoform       1.59
Quartz          1.54—1.55
                (0.009)
Canada balsam 1.53
Xylene          1.49

*4th test* — Fluorescence.

The fluorescent effects of diamonds under u.v. light are variable. Some stones seem virtually inert, some glow a pale violet, others emit sky blue fluorescence, and a few a yellow fluorescence.

In the main these effects have little value in actually identifying individual diamonds but there is one exception. Stones showing strong blue fluorescence under long wave ultra-violet light and a yellow after-glow when quickly removed from the lamp, are definitely diamond.

A table of the fluorescent effects of the diamond simulants is appended.

|                    | *L.W.*        | *S.W.*                |
|--------------------|---------------|-----------------------|
| Y.A.G.             | Yellow        | Yellow                |
| Scheelite          |               | Whitish Blue          |
| Synthetic spinel   | Green         | White                 |
| Synthetic sapphire | Green (weak)  |                       |
| Natural sapphire   | Orange        | Orange                |
| G.G.G.             | Pale yellow   | Peach (with spectrum) |

71

*5th test* — Spectroscope examination.

This is quite a specialised technique and one requiring quite a considerable amount of practice.

Most diamonds exhibit a narrow absorption band in the deep violet (4155A) and when seen it is a positive test for diamond. In some diamonds this band is very strong and is accompanied by other weaker, bands.

The effect is best seen when light (preferably blue light from the copper sulphate solution) is transmitted through the stone sideways, i.e., parallel to the table facet of the stone.

Spectrum effects likely to be seen in the diamond simulants are as follows:

White zircons generally show a strong line in the red (6535A) and a fainter one nearby (6590A). Sometimes other lines of the zircon spectrum, discussed later in the section concerned with identification of this stone, may also be seen.

Synthetic scheelite sometimes exhibits a very strong spectrum consisting of a group, or number of groups, of very fine lines.

Some specimens of blende may have narrow absorption bands in the red.

Synthetic rutile shows a very strong line in the violet (4250A) of the spectrum.

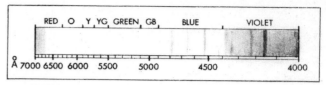

DIAMOND spectrum

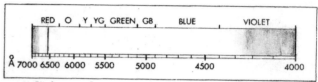

ZIRCON spectrum

# DIAMOND SIMULANTS

A list of positive tests for the stones likely to be used as diamond simulants is now added and may be carried out should the stone under test be now considered other than diamond, or should there still be an element of doubt.

It is, of course, possible to carry out all these tests in rotation, working on the assumption that any stone "failing" all the tests will almost certainly be diamond.

*1st test* —Polariscope.

All stones showing clear doubly refractive effects on the polariscope may be eliminated as possible diamonds, as may those which show clear doubling of the back facets whether with naked eye, 10x lens or microscope.

*2nd test* For doubly-refractive stones.

On the refractometer the following results will confirm the identity of the stone.

| | | |
|---|---|---|
| 1.54—1.55 | quartz (rock crystal) | No other test is required |
| 1.61—1.62 | topaz | No other test required |
| 1.76—1.77 | sapphire (either natural or synthetic) | Test under microscope for signs of natural inclusions which would prove the stone natural, or for signs of bubbles to identify the synthetic. Test under ultra-violet light, where natural stones exhibit an orange fluorescence under both long and short-wave whereas synthetic sapphires emit a weak green effect under long-wave only. |

When the refractometer scale is in complete shadow, proving that the stone has a higher refractive index than 1.81, the stone may be scheelite if it fluoresces whitish-blue under short-wave ultra-violet light. Zircon will be identified by its spectrum, as already stated, while the two remaining doubly refractive stones to be considered, lithium niobate and synthetic rutile, may be separated by the fact that rutile has a very strong line in the violet of the spectrum (4250A) and has far greater doubling of the back facets in addition to which it always possesses a distinct yellow colour tinge.

*2nd test* — For singly refractive stones.

Under short-wave ultra-violet light, synthetic colourless spinel will glow with a vivid white-green fluorescence, after which its identity may be confirmed with a refractometer reading of 1.727.

Also under ultra-violet light of short wavelength, gadolinium gallium garnet (G.G.G.), a recent synthetic, emits a peach-coloured fluorescence. When examined through the spectroscope, this gives what is called a fluorescence spectrum, consisting of strong absorption in the red, accompanied by a bright line, another bright line where the yellow should be, two distinct bands in the green and two in the blue.

*3rd test* — Immersion test.

If the stone is suspected of being a synthetic yttrium aluminium garnet (Y.A.G.), it may be immersed in liquid provided with the refractometer (1.81), in which it will virtually disappear.

Another distinctive feature of Y.A.G.s is that if the stones are examined through the table facet with the stone tilted at an angle of about 45° the pavilion facets (that would be clearly visible if the gem was a diamond) disappear, and a dark cloud seems to pass through this section of the stone.

*4th test* — Internal examination.

Paste imitations may often be identified by their inclusion of bubbles. If present in a stone, confirmation of its identity as paste may be made by obtaining a refractive index reading on the refractometer of between 1.47 and 1.70.

The other two possible diamond simulants, strontium titanate and blende will not be easily identified, but the high dispersion and softness of strontium and the even greater softness of blende, makes the separation of these stones from diamond a simple matter that should have been carrried out in the first two paragraphs of this section.

# DIOPSIDE

This gemstone is generally bottle green in colour although white, brown and violet-blue stones are known. Cat's eyes and star stones are also found but are dealt with under the relevant headings.

*1st test* — Polariscope: Necessary result, double refraction.

*2nd test* — Refractometer.

The average reading for diopside is 1.670 — 1.700 with a distinctive birefringence of 0.030.

There should be little difficulty in identifying the stones owing to the birefringence. Perhaps the only stone to be wary of is sinhalite, which has a similar R.I. but greater double refraction (0.036).

*Other tests* — Spectroscopic analysis.

The brighter green stones generally have a fairly distinctive absorption spectrum.

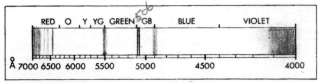

Green DIOPSIDE spectrum

# EMERALD

Emerald of a fine grass-green colour and of reasonable clarity is a rare and valuable gemstone. For this reason a lot of work has gone towards the manufacture of synthetic stones, and it is the separation of these from natural emerald which provides the gemmologist with most of his problems with respect to this material.

*1st test* — Polariscope: Necessary result, double refraction.

*2nd test* — Refractometer.

On the refractometer two readings should be obtained, for both natural and synthetic stones, between 1.56 and 1.60, with a birefringence of not less than 0.005, and not more than 0.009. It should be noted that many of the synthetic emeralds on the market possess a birefringence of between 0.002 and 0.004, so that any emerald having this characteristic should be suspect.

A positive R.I. result along the lines described above will prove the stone to be either natural or synthetic emerald or a composite stone with a crown of natural beryl (i.e. aquamarine or colourless beryl).

*3rd test* — Surface examination

The stone should now be carefully examined, with the 10x lens, for signs of a join around the girdle, which would prove the stone to be composite (stones made of two or more pieces in an attempt to imitate emerald, are sometimes called "soudé emeralds"). It is a good plan to immerse the stone in a liquid of reasonably high R.I. and examine against a white background whilst holding the stone sideways on in the liquid. If it is a doublet, the stone will normally show a strong green join mark along the girdle and be colourless above and below.

Should this effect be seen, the stone may be safely identified as imitation.

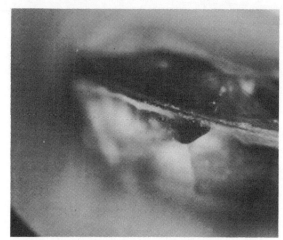

EMERALD doublet with emerald top and base glued together

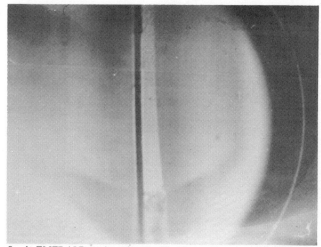

Soudé EMERALD in the refractive liquid test. The stone is immersed in water; it clearly shows the coloured layer of cement surrounded by colourless material

*4th test* — Microscopic analysis.

The only positive method of ascertaining whether the stone is natural or synthetic, if it has "passed" the 3rd test satisfactorily, is by microscopic analysis of the internal features of the stone. Many explanatory photographs will be found in the following pages.

*Other tests*

*Absorption Spectrum*

Emeralds (both natural and synthetic) show an absorption spectrum consisting of two or more fine lines in the red, a rather weak band in the yellow and general absorption of the violet. In the weaker coloured stones only the lines in the red can be seen and then only faintly.

*Chelsea colour filter*

The majority, but not all, of natural emeralds emit a red glow when viewed through the Chelsea colour filter, which may vary from a dull to quite bright effect.

Most, but not all, synthetic emeralds also show red through the filter, but in general a much brighter colour than natural stones.

The majority, but not all, of emerald imitations appear dull green or inert when examined through the filter, exceptions being demantoid garnets, fine green fluorite, green zircons and even some soudé emeralds, all of which may show reddish.

It will be seen from the foregoing that, contrary to popular belief, the Chelsea colour filter is of precious little use in the identification of emerald today. It was introduced after the soudé emerald came on the market.

*Ultra-violet light*

Emeralds show similar effects to those described immediately above, when irradiated by both long and short-

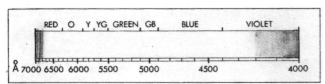

Weak EMERALD spectrum

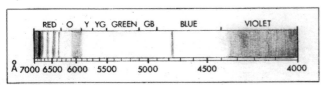

Rich EMERALD spectrum

wave ultra-violet light, but the results are a little more conclusive as most natural stones are inert or show only a dull red fluorescence whereas most synthetics show quite a distinctive red glow. On top of this most of the stones which are likely to be confused with emerald and which appear red through the Chelsea filter are inert under ultra-violet light, or fluoresce a different colour from emerald.

EMERALD The best known inclusion in natural stones is the three-phase inclusion — a liquid, a gas bubble and a salt cube — these are mostly very small. Here is a series of inclusions x 10

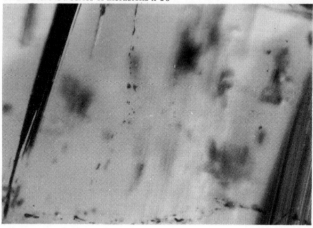

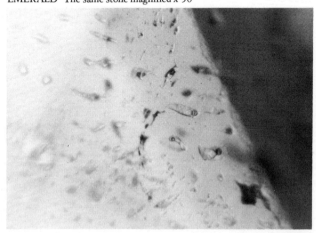

EMERALD  The same stone magnified x 50

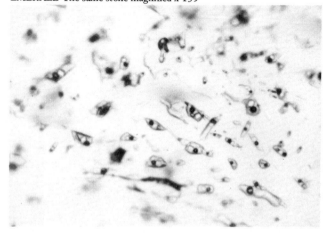

EMERALD The same stone magnified x 135

EMERALD  A single inclusion from the same stone

EMERALD  'Comma' two-phase inclusions in a stone from India

EMERALD  These peculiar feathers are typical of natural stones, though not distinctive of emeralds

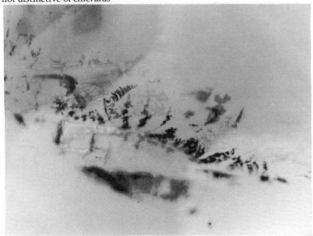

EMERALD  A distinctive pattern of needle inclusions, plus an occasional rectangular two-phase inclusion. The needles are in pairs, intersecting at rightangles and in series

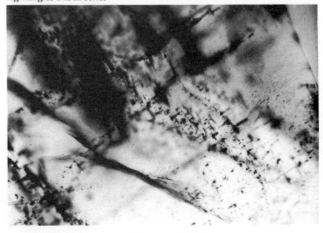

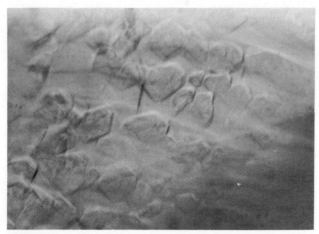

EMERALD Interesting markings of roughly hexagonal outline as a result of growth disturbances

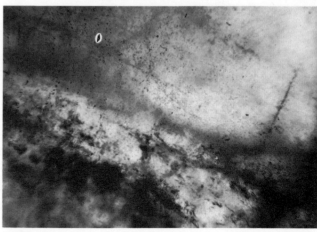

EMERALD A multitude of tiny, irregular, opaque particles makes this natural stone cloudy. There are many stones like this on the market at present

EMERALD A Columbian stone containing well-formed transparent calcite crystals

EMERALD Another Columbian stone containing a well-shaped pyrite crystal. The three-phase inclusions that surround it make what is called a 'jardin'

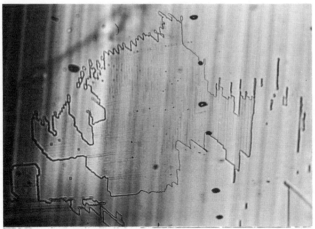

EMERALD Another Brazilian stone containing an ultra-flat fluid film with jagged edges

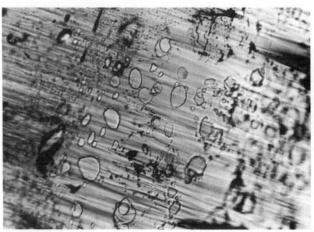

EMERALD Brazilian stones often contain these very fine films of one and two-phase inclusions in front of parallel striations

EMERALD Stones from the Ural Mountains in Russia are the only ones to contain actinolite crystals of this type. They have cracks across them and resemble bamboo stalks

EMERALD Tremolite needles are only found in Sandawana emeralds from Rhodesia

EMERALD These densely-packed actinolite crystals are typical of a Habachthal stone from Austria

EMERALD Another Habachthal stone, densely-packed with tiny biotite flakes. These emeralds are no longer mined but examples are numerous

Synthetic EMERALD Most synthetic stones are fairly cloudy due to the inclusion of many veil-like feathers. Under low magnification, they seem to be of irregular structure

Synthetic EMERALD The same stone, under higher magnification, shows the feathers twist and intersect in a kind of network. The stone is by Chatham

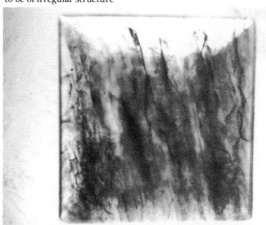

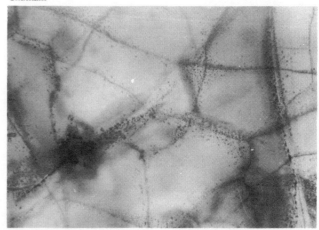

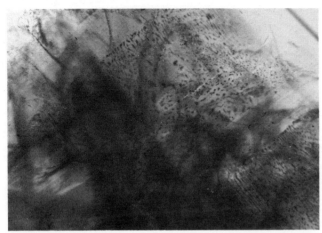

Synthetic EMERALD Little crystal shapes can sometimes be seen among the veils

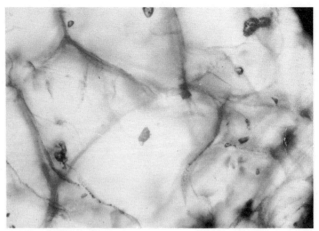

Synthetic EMERALD These phenakite crystals are rather larger

Synthetic EMERALD Under high magnification, some feathers consists of myriads of two-phase inclusions. Note that two-phase inclusions in synthetic stones are normally rounded and bear no regular relationship to each other; in natural stones, they are either flat-sided or spiky-edged, and are often in parallel formation

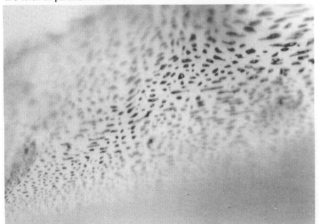

Synthetic EMERALD Under higher magnification, this French stone by Gilson shows the two-phase inclusions that form the veil-like feathers

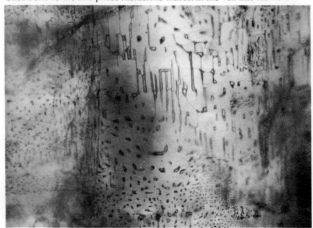

Synthetic EMERALD This stone has two well-formed phenakite crystals proving that crystal inclusions are not exclusive to natural emeralds

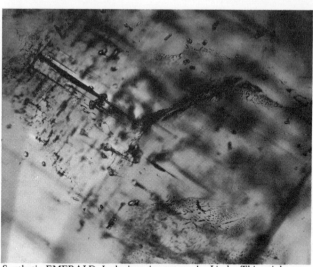

Synthetic EMERALD Inclusions in a stone by Linde. This might seem natural at first glance but the inclusions look like nails

Synthetic EMERALD A stronger impression of the nail-like inclusions in a Linde stone

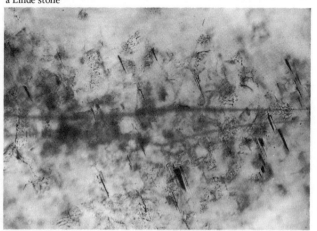

Synthetic EMERALD This is an 'Emerita': a beryl with a layer of synthetic emerald deposited on it. The picture shows the crazing cracks in the synthetic layer. They were made by Lechleitner of Austria

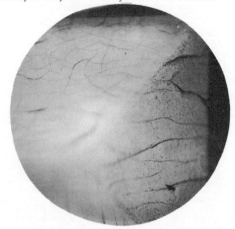

# ENSTATITE

Green or brownish-green stones of this mineral are occasionally encountered, and also cat's-eyes (dealt with under that heading).

*1st test* — Polariscope: Necessary result, double refraction.

*2nd test* — Refractometer.

A refractometer reading of 1.66 — 1.67 and bi-refringence of 0.010 should be obtained. Both shadow edges move with change of direction. Sometimes the R.I. can be a little higher but the birefringence is constant.

*3rd test* — Spectroscope.

Enstatite has a distinctive absorption spectrum of one sharp line at the lower end of the green (5060A) accompanied by a fainter line almost in the yellow part of the green (5500A) and a number of faint bands in the red. Further bands may be seen in the blue and violet end of the spectrum, but these are not easy to see owing to the intensity of the line in the green.

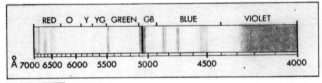

ENSTATITE spectrum

# FIRE OPAL

Fire opal is a transparent gemstone possessing a vivid orange-red coloration that can be imagined by reviving memories of the flames given off by a coal fire.

*1st test* — Polariscope: Necessary result, single refraction.

*2nd test* — Refractive index.

The refractive index of fire opal varies between 1.44 and 1.46 and is distinctive, no glass or plastic imitation having the same reading. If the stone has a flat facet, a refractometer reading will be easily obtained but as many of the stones have domed surfaces it will mean resorting to the distant vision method or, often more satisfactory, immersion tests. Fire opal, immersed in carbon tetrachloride, which has a refractive index of 1.46, will become virtually invisible with the exception of its colour, the facet edges of the stone completely losing their definition. On the other hand, imitation stones under the same conditions will have edges which stand out with reasonable definition.

### Other test

*Spectroscopic analysis*

The absorption spectrum of fire opal shows the whole spectrum, except the red and orange, in shadow, the edge of the shadow being broad and indistinct.

The orange glass often used to imitate fire opal has a similar spectrum but the shadow edge is sharper and more distinct.

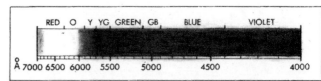

FIRE OPAL spectrum

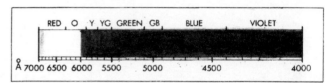

Orange GLASS spectrum (imitation fire opal)

# RED GARNETS

The family of gemstones known as garnets consists of a wide range of colours, the most common being various shades of red. In this section the identification of the red, lilac and violet-red stones will be considered, the green (demantoid and chrome grossular) and brown (hessonite) stones being dealt with separately under their own headings.

The garnet species consists of an isomorphous series of gemstones. This, very roughly, means that the chemical composition of the stones concerned can vary from one to another without alteration of their basic structure, so that it is possible to have two stones, with slightly different composition, related to each other because of their similar internal form.

Generally the members of an isomorphous series can be split into sub-sections, and in the garnet species they are as follows:—

| | |
|---|---|
| Pyrope | Blood red when pure. |
| Almandine | Violet red when pure. |
| Spessartite | Yellow when pure. |
| Grossular | Best known as orange-red or brownish-red and called Hessonite. |
| Andradite | Best known as grass green and called Demantoid. |
| Uvarovite | Almost unknown as a gem. |

It is very rare for a garnet to be found which can be ascribed to any one of these sub-groups alone, the majority of garnets being a mixture of two or more types in varying proportions.

The reason behind this brief excursion into theory in a work devoted to practical things is that the wide variations of chemical composition which are possible in the garnet species due to isomorphous replacement leads to equally wide variations of optical effects such as refractive index, and an understanding of this is desirable before identification of garnets may be easily carried out.

*1st test* — Spectroscopic analysis.

Red, lilac, violet or violet-red stones suspected of being garnets should immediately be subjected to spectroscopic analysis, as by far the majority of them possess enough almandine content in their make-up to produce an absorption spectrum which is distinctive to a degree high enough to make identification positive.

The most satisfactory method of viewing this spectrum is to transmit a powerful beam of light through the stone and analyse this with the spectroscope. The method gives more consistent results than the method of placing the stone table facet down on a dark material and viewing light reflected from the inside of this facet.

The spectrum seen, if the stone is garnet, is a group of three bands, one each in the yellow (5760A), green (5270A) and blue-green (5050A) accompanied by two weaker bands, one in the orange (6170A) and the other in the blue (4620A).

It should be noted that, of the three main bands, the one in the blue-green is the broadest and strongest and the one in the yellow next strongest, and that the weakest of the three bands is not equidistant between the other two but a little nearer the blue-green band. In many garnets these three bands alone may be seen by the transmitted light method and often quite weakly, but they are so distinctive even on their own as to prove the gem to contain almandine garnet.

On the other hand, some stones show all the five bands mentioned in great relative strength along with another weaker one in the blue (4760A), and the intensity of absorption in the blue-green is such that the two bands there become almost as one very broad band.

Some fine blood-red garnets contain a high proportion of pyrope to the exclusion of most almandine with the result that only the strongest almandine band can be clearly seen,

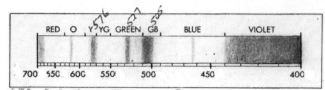

ALMANDINE GARNET spectrum

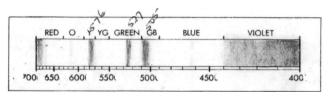

Weak ALMANDINE GARNET spectrum

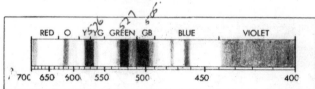

Strong ALMANDINE GARNET spectrum

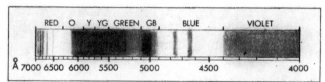

PYROPE GARNET spectrum

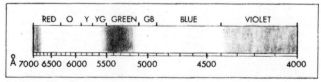

Selenium GLASS spectrum

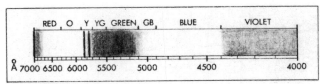

Selenium GLASS spectrum

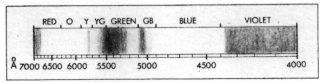

GARNET-TOPPED DOUBLET spectrum

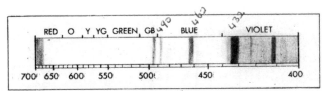

SPESSARTITE GARNET spectrum

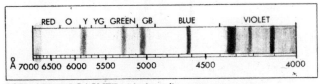

SPESSARTITE GARNET with almandine content spectrum

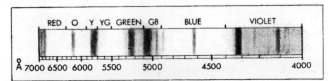

SPESSARTITE-ALMANDINE GARNET spectrum

as the pyrope causes a broad absorption band which covers all the yellow and most of the green. In addition it may be possible to see fine lines in the red.

Care needs to be taken here because there are many red glass imitation stones about, which are coloured by an element called selenium. This produces a spectrum which consists sometimes of a broad band in the green and more rarely, with fine lines due to another element incorporated into this band.

These stones should not cause much confusion when familiarity has been gained with the garnet spectrum. A gem tester can be caught, however, by a rather cute imitation, of which there are many about, which consists of a red glass stone with a piece of almandine garnet fused to the top. This imitation stone exhibits a spectrum consisting of a combination of selenium and weak almandine.

Spessartite garnets are rarely found yellow, but generally orange or browny-red. The spectrum of pure spessartite consists of a strong band in the violet (4320A), a weaker one just in the blue (4620A), and two weak lines in the green-blue (4890A and 4950A). Deep in the violet a fine band at 4240A and a powerful one at 4120A may be seen by those whose vision is strong at that end of the spectrum.

Occasionally stones may be encountered which are mainly spessartite but with a small percentage of almandine, so that the main almandine bands will be seen.

More commonly the stone may be found to possess bands of the two types in what appear to be equal proportions.

Familiarity with these spectra, and confidence in their use, will be found to save a lot of time. For example the oft quoted problem of identifying a batch of 100 mixed red stones will be quickly put in hand if all the garnets are separated with the spectroscope in about five minutes, as this is the time it would take an expert to examine the spectra of all the stones.

Before proceeding to the next text, it may be worth pointing out that the polariscope is not of great benefit when test-

89

ing garnets. In the first place, many of the stones that may be confused with them possess the same singly refractive effect as the garnets themselves. In the second place, whereas the majority of garnets show a singly refractive effect on the polariscope, quite a large proportion exhibit an anomalous effect and a small percentage show clear double refraction.

*2nd test* — Refractometer.

As previously mentioned, a wide variation of refractive index readings is possible, owing to isomorphous replacement. Nevertheless, R.I. has a definite testing value with garnets of a red hue, particularly when combined with other information, in an attempt to identify the type of garnet.

The range of refractive index possible with red garnets is from 1.730 to 1.81, and the particular readings obtained from each type are as follows:—

| | |
|---|---|
| Pyrope | 1.730 to 1.750 |
| Pyrope/Almandine intermediate series | 1.75 to 1.78 |
| Almandine | 1.78 to 1.80 |
| Spessartite | 1.79 to 1.81 |
| Rhodolite | 1.745 to 1.760 |

Where two types overlap with regard to refractive index, other tests will be necessary to identify them. A garnet with an R.I. in the rhodolite/pyrope/intermediate region will be judged by its spectrum (rhodolites have an almandine absorption whereas pyropes have their own) and by its inclusions (see next test). Spessartites may be separated from almandine by colour and spectrum.

*3rd test* — Microscopic analysis.

The inclusions to be found in garnets are wide and varied, some are distinctive, and familiarity should be gained with all of them as this test can be of great benefit in the testing of stones set in closed back jewellery of the Georgian and Victorian type.

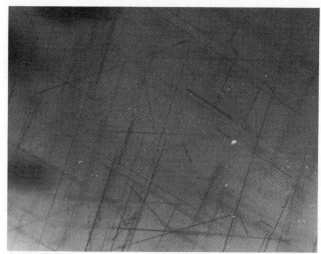

GARNET Strong black needles are a common inclusion in garnets with a high almandine content; there may be only a few or a great number. They can be short or cross the crystal; they can intersect in parallel in two or more directions or be erratically dispersed

GARNET Opaque black masses with crystal outlines commonly accompany the needles

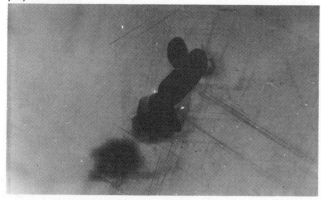

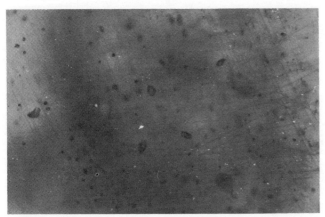

GARNET  The crystal inclusions can also be more transparent

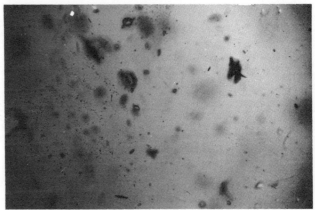

GARNET  These 'zircon-halo' inclusions are typical of stones from Sri Lanka. They are surrounded by stress marks, hence the 'halo': they are also compared to bees in flight

GARNET  This stone is densely packed with mainly opaque crystals

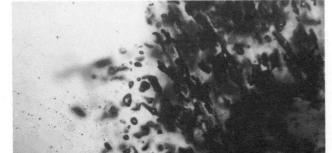

GARNET  These inclusions are mainly transparent

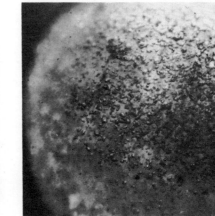

# GLASS IMITATIONS

Glass gemstones can be made to imitate virtually any gem material. Generally they are easily identified.

*1st test* — Polariscope: Necessary result, single refraction.

Often an anomalous effect is produced, typically a cross-like shadow which is static in relationship to the polariscope when the stone is rotated.

*2nd test* — Refractometer: between 1.45 and 1.69.

It should be noted that there is no singly refractive transparent natural gemstone with refractive index between 1.50 and 1.70, so the R.I. is decisive in the majority of cases.

## *Other tests*

### *Microscopic analysis and 10x lens examination*

Bubbles are a very common inclusion in glass. Often one or more large, spherical ones may be seen as shown. Swirls of very small bubbles also occur.

Bubbles may be seen with either a 10x lens or a microscope. It should be borne in mind that many bubbles occurring in one plane (layer) would indicate a join between two substances and that the stone might be composite.

Another common feature of glass imitations is an effect called striae. This is a little like the effect seen in stirred golden syrup and is distinctive. The author has always found the effect most easily seen with a 10x lens. But see hessonite garnet.

### *Tongue test*

Glass is a bad conductor of heat and if touched by the tongue will feel warm, whereas natural and synthetic gem-

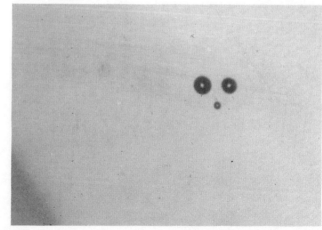

GLASS bubbles

stones will feel cold. This test requires a certain amount of care to be correctly carried out. To begin with the stone must be clean, if only for hygiene considerations. Secondly the stone must be already cool, i.e. left for a while in a cool atmosphere to ensure that it has not already become artificially warm. Third, the stone must not be held by the fingers, as this will warm it before the test is carried out, but by the metal of its setting if it has one, or by stone tongs.

GLASS bubble striae

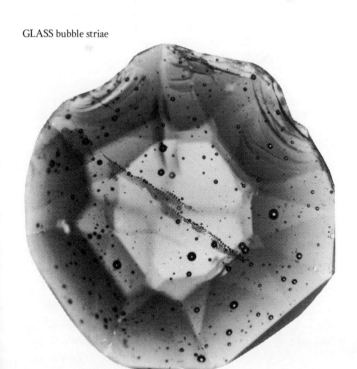

GLASS striae

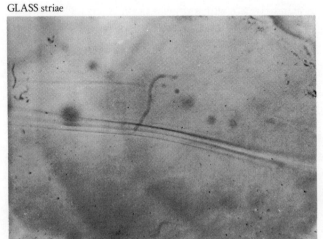

# HESSONITE GARNET

The colour most normally associated with hessonite garnet is orange-brown, but yellow-brown and red-brown are also possible. Most competent gemmologists, on being faced with a stone of hessonite appearance, would immediately look for inclusions, as these are so distinctive that the stone may generally be identified by internal appearance alone. In more average circles, however, the following series of tests is recommended.

*1st test* — Polariscope: Necessary result, single refraction.

*2nd test* — Refractometer: 1.745 approx.
This reading is constant to within two to three third decimal places either way.

*3rd test* — Microscopic analysis.
As mentioned before, the inclusions in hessonites are distinctive, and best seen under low power magnification or even by 10x lens. The internal structure has been described as akin to treacle with swirl effects and many inclusions, the majority of which are transparent. Note that glass (paste) can also have syrup-like inclusions.

*Other tests*

*Spectroscopic anaylsis*
Examination of the absorption spectrum of hessonites is not of great benefit as the only features likely to be seen are weak bands attributable to almandine garnet, traces of which are almost always contained in hessonite.

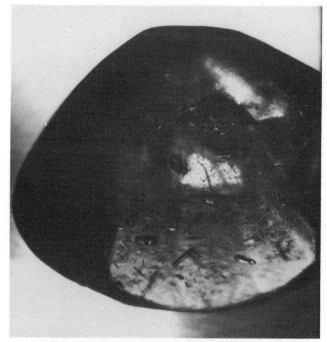

HESSONITE GARNET inclusions
HESSONITE GARNET inclusions

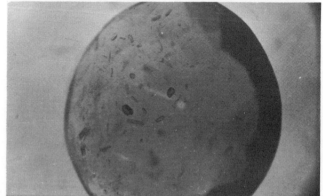

94

# IOLITE

Iolite is found in colours similar to blue sapphire but its refractive index is so distinct that it can hardly be confused.

*1st test* — Polariscope: Necessary result, double refraction.

*2nd test* — Refractometer: between 1.53 and 1.55 with a bi-refringence between 0.008 and 0.012.

*3rd test* — Dichroism.
Iolite possesses extremely strong pleochroism, so strong that it may be seen even without the use of the dichroscope by viewing the stone from various directions while holding it between the eye and a strong light source. In one direction the stone will appear almost colourless, while in a direction at right angles to this, a rich blue colour will be seen.

By examining the stone in various directions with the dichroscope, it should be possible to see three different colours, pale yellow, light blue, and dark violet-blue.

*Other test* — Spectrum analysis.
The absorption spectrum of iolite is quite rich but not strong. Fairly narrow bands may be seen: one in the red (6450A), a pair in the yellow (5930, 5850A), one in the green (5350A), a stronger one in the blue (4920A), and three others in the blue and violet (4560, 4360 and 4260A).

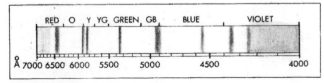

IOLITE spectrum

# IVORY

The beautiful white to creamy yellow opaque material called ivory, which comes from tusks of elephants, may be identified by close examination of its surface. In one direction, it exhibits curved intersecting growth lines of alternatively lighter and darker colour, which has the appearance of the engine-turned pattern often seen on small silver articles such as cigarette cases and dressing table pieces. This effect is not seen on imitations and is proof of the article being true elephant ivory.

As a confirmatory test, a hydrostatic specific gravity between 1.70 and 1.90 should be obtained where practical if the piece is large enough. Be careful to ensure that the calculation is not ruined by air bubbles being captured in any delicate carving that may decorate the material. Air bubbles can generally be eliminated by wetting the article, brushing water into any cavities with a soft brush, immersing the article and giving it a final brush whilst held under water.

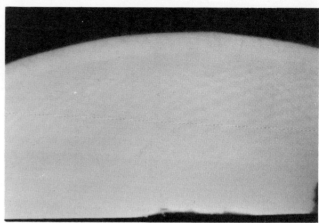
IVORY surface

# JADE

There are two separate minerals either of which may be correctly called jade, their individual names being jadeite and nephrite. As they have slightly different optical and physical properties it is convenient to discuss them separately, as it may be necessary to ascertain which member of the jade family a particular piece belongs to.

# NEPHRITE

Nephrite is a translucent to opaque material, the colour of which may vary from very pale whitish-green through various tints of green to rich, deep green. Yellow and brown nephrite is also found and a common occurrence in all the material is crack-like vein markings which in older pieces take on a ''rusted'' colour.

The positive identification of nephrite is a difficult proposition these days without the use of costly laboratory apparatus, but a strong opinion may be formed by examining the following factors.

*1st test* — Refractometer.

A vague refractive index reading of 1.62, by distant vision method if necessary, should be obtained.

*2nd test* — (where practical) Specific gravity.

The gemmologist is often confronted with small carvings and these lend themselves quite readily to hydrostatic specific gravity calculations, if the piece is large enough, using spring scales and tap water. The result obtained should be between 2.95 and 3.00, although 2.90 and 3.05 are permissible extremes, bearing in mind slight inaccuracies caused by the method used.

There is little else to do by way of practical tests. The absorption spectrum is generally indistinct, although occasionally a doublet in the red may be seen and/or bands in the blue/violet, but it is doubtful whether these could be called distinctive. For the rest, familiarity with the general appearance of the material and careful scrutinisation of the section devoted to describing materials likely to be used as jade simulants, is about as much as can be done.

# JADEITE

Jadeite is translucent to opaque and may be found in virtually any colour. The most prized is the translucent grass green material.

*1st test* — Refractometer.

As with nephrite, it may be necessary to use the distant vision technique where a vague reading of about 1.66 should be obtained. If a flat face is available it is often possible to get two readings at 1.654 and 1.667.

*2nd test* — Specific gravity.

If practical, a specific gravity test by hydrostatic method should be carried out and should result in a figure of a little over 3.30, not higher than 3.36. It may be noted that this reading is very close to the specific gravity of methylene iodide so that a small unset piece could be tested in this liquid and, if jadeite, should remain virtually suspended when placed in the centre.

*3rd test* — Spectrum analysis.

Fortunately the absorption spectrum of jadeite is stronger and more diagnostic than nephrite. It consists of a line in the blue/violet (4375A) of great strength, which is diagnostic, and generally some weaker bands, one either side. In the fine grass green jadeite there is general absorption of the violet which may mask the 4375 line, but in this case equally distinctive lines in the red will be found.

Satisfactory results from these two sets of tests cannot be taken as conclusive evidence of the material being jade unfortunately, and some indication is now given of some of the cunning ways in which the gemmologist may be deceived.

1. Jadeite may be stained, most commonly green, but other colours are possible. Often the colour penetrates the cracks

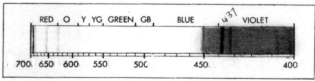

JADEITE spectrum

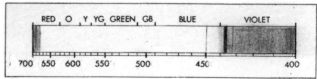

JADEITE with iron content spectrum

in the material, but not always. The absorption spectrum of the treated stone may show two bands in the red, which are proof of staining.

2. Jade may be "improved" by sticking two pieces together with green cement, the colour from the cement permeating the whole stone. These imitations are extremely difficult to detect when the join mark, which is generally around the outside edges of a cabochon stone, is hidden by the setting. Such stones may also show the two bands in the red of the spectrum.

3. There are many natural materials which may be confused with jade by appearance alone, but provided either refractive index or specific gravity checks can be made very few should cause much trouble. The material called sausserite is one exception. It is a rock which generally has different R.I.s in different directions and in different coloured sections. A small uniform coloured stone could be difficult, and if doubt still exists after spectrum analysis (sausserite may have lines in the red, a line or absorption in the violet, or no lines or absorption at all), then the stone should be subjected to thorough laboratory tests if a positive identification is necessary.

If refractive index alone is to be relied upon when testing, then two other materials must be considered, smithsonite, which shows a vague shadow edge at 1.62, and prehnite, R.I. 1.63. Smithsonite may be eliminated by placing a small drop of *weak* hydrochloric acid on its surface, which will cause effervescence. Prehnite has a radiating fibrous structure which is quite distinctive.

The table below shows the refractive index and specific gravity of materials with a jade-like appearance so that identification may be completed.

| Material | R.I. | S.G. | Other remarks |
|---|---|---|---|
| Amazonite | 1.53 | 2.56 | distinctive sheen |
| Chalcedony | 1.54 | 2.60 | |
| Aventurine quartz | 1.55 | 2.67 | |

| | | |
|---|---|---|
| Bowenite (serpentine) | 1.55 to 1.56 | 2.59 |
| Williamsite (serpentine) | 1.57 | 2.61 |
| Pseudophite (serpentine) | 1.57 | 2.69 |
| Smithsonite | 1.62 | 4.35 |
| Prehnite | 1.63 | 2.90 |
| **Saussurite** variable | | 2.90 to 3.10 |
| Californite (massive idocrase) | 1.72 | 3.30 |
| Grossular garnet (massive) | 1.73 | 3.48 |

# JET

Jet is a black, opaque, fossilized wood, similar to coal, which although soft, takes a magnificent polish. It is often carved as beads, lockets, pendants and cameos.

The surest method of identification is to touch an inconspicuous part of the object with a hot needle, when jet will give off a smell of burning coal whereas plastic imitations smell like burning hair or rubber or are inert. Glass, of course, will be unaffected by this treatment.

# KORNERUPINE

This stone is occasionally found in green shades, generally pale, and in deep browny-green.

*1st test* — Polariscope: Necessary result, double refraction.

*2nd test* — Refractometer.
The refractive index of kornerupine is generally between 1.665 and 1.680 with a birefrigence of 0.013.

*Other tests*

*Dichroism*
Kornerupine shows strong dichroism, the colours seen with the dichroscope being green and either yellow or brown.

*Spectroscopic analysis*
The spectrum is generally fairly weak but may help as a confirmatory test.

The most distinctive signs are a weak, fairly broad band in the green part of the spectrum (5030A) and a narrow but often rather more distinct line in the violet (4460A). One or two other very weak lines may be seen around the blue and violet.

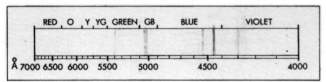

KORNERUPINE spectrum

# LAPIS LAZULI

The magnificent azure blue colour of the finest lapis lazuli is its sole reason for popularity. It is an opaque material and its composition is of interest because it is not a single mineral but a rock, i.e. a combination of a number of different minerals.

The colour of lapis is caused by the inclusion of the minerals hauynite, sodalite and lazurite, while there is also a certain amount of calcite present, which produces white speckles, and iron pyrite, which is seen as brassy speckles.

*1st test* — Lens examination.

Close examination of the surface of the material with a 10x lens is perhaps the best test for lapis. It will generally be possible to find some specks of pyrites (not a certain test as the stone sodalite is also found with pyrites embedded) and also the patches of white caused by the calcite. It may be necessary to resort to the microscope to find these. This irregular mottled surface structure, seen with the 10x lens and more easily by microscope, is distinctive.

*2nd test* — Refractometer.

A shadow edge at about 1.50 should be seen. With cabochon cut stones it will be necessary to use the distant vision technique, but in any case the author has found that the best results are to be obtained by the distant vision technique, using a corner or edge of the stone.

*Other tests*

*Chelsea colour filter* — Dull brownish red.
*Long wave ultra violet light* — Mainly inert but with specks or streaks of a dull orange tint.

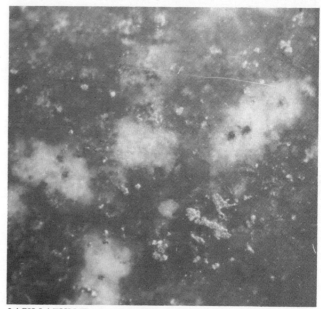

LAPIS LAZULI The brassy specks of pyriates stand out in this picture of the surface of this stone; the white patches are calcite

102

*Short wave ultra-violet light* — Similar to the effects seen under long wave but weaker and perhaps more pinkish in tint.

## MOONSTONE

The gemstone called moonstone is in fact a member of the large group of stones called feldspars. Moonstone is transparent to translucent, colourless or delicate shades of pink, green or blue, and is regarded highly for the milky or pearly reflections which occur from inside the stone.

*1st test* — Polariscope: Necessary result, double refraction.

*2nd test* — Refractometer.
As the stones are invariably cabochon cut to show off the sheen to the best effect, the distant vision technique will be necessary and a refractive index reading of 1.53, approximately, should be obtained.

*Other test*

*Microscopic analysis*
The distinctive appearance of moonstone in association with the two tests described above is generally quite enough evidence with which to identify the stones. Moonstones often possess tiny stress cracks which are so interesting and distinctive, when seen through the microscope, that it is well worth while looking for them.

MOONSTONE crazing

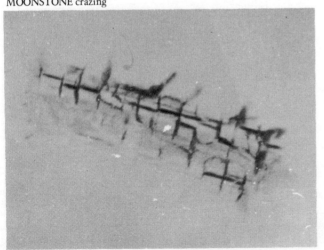

# MORGANITE

This pale pink transparent member of the beryl gem species may be easily confused with pink spodumene at sight.

*1st test* — Polariscope: Necessary result, double refraction.

*2nd test* — Refractometer.

The average refractive index for morganite is 1.58 to 1.59 but may be as high as 1.60 for the upper shadow edge. The birefringence may be 0.008 or 0.009.

*Other tests*

*Dichroscope* — Distinct dichroism can be seen, pale pink and deep pink being the two colours.

*Ultra-violet light* — A weak lilac glow should be evident.

*Microscopic analysis*

These stones are generally quite clear, but elongated cavities, like canals, and two phase inclusions, both types similar to the inclusions seen in aquamarine, are possible.

# OPAL

*White opal*

The white opals used in jewellery have a creamy white body colour, are mainly opaque, although some translucent stones are found which could be classed as white opals, but most important they show the fascinating effect of reflecting variegated colours from their surface. The finest quality

Synthetic OPAL These three enlargements show the surface structure of synthetic opal. The light patches are from the areas of brilliant red reflection and are distinctive by the abrupt termination of the colour patches and the general hexagonal surface etch-marks

Synthetic OPAL

Synthetic OPAL

opals reflect all the colours of the spectrum whereas the cheaper varieties reflect only one or more colours. The surface appearance of white opal is so distinctive that no tests are required, as the only stones which could possibly confuse are glass imitations so poor that even a cursory examination will spot them. All the colour play in these stones is underneath the surface whereas the colour-play of true opal is a surface effect.

A synthetic opal is now being produced, which has similar physical and optical properties to the natural stone.

*Black opal*

As with the white variety, no testing of the normal type is necessary with black opal as there is no imitation likely to be confused with the real material, so that a potential black opal needs to be sorted into one of the following four types.

1. Natural.
2. Doublet or triplet.
3. Treated opal.
4. Synthetic opal.

The treated stones on the market have generally such a mottled irregular play of colour. It is so distinct from the effect seen in natural stones that visual examination should be all that is necessary.

Doublets (composed of a thin slice of natural black opal cemented onto a base of either onyx, low quality opal or some other similar material) and triplets (basically the same as doublets but with a layer of transparent rock crystal or some other similar material fitted on the top to prevent damage to the opal) are easily identified when loose, as the join between layers is evident around the edge of the stone. However, many of these stones are set in such a way that the edge cannot be seen and in this case the following points may be considered.

a. If the underneath of the stone can be examined and if the stone has an onyx base, it can be safely decided that the stone is not natural.

b. If the stone is closely inspected from directly above with 10x lens or microscope, and an attempt made to look into the stone, it may be possible to see bubbles caught in the cement used to join the two pieces. These may appear as discs inside the stone. It may help to shine a strong light from underneath the stone, or even from as nearly overhead as possible.

c. Triplets will have a glassy surface appearance and if one is closely examined with a 10x lens it will be seen that the play of colour is not a surface effect. If doubt arises, a distant vision refractive index reading will give a result of about 1.54 (if rock crystal is the material used for the top surface) whereas opal has a R.I. of 1.45. Some triplets have a glass top, when the reading will be in the range for glass.

## Synthetic opal

Synthetic opal is produced by the firm of Gilson, in France. At first sight the polished stones are just like natural ones. Identification may be carried out as follows:

*1st test* — Examination by naked eye and 10x lens. The synthetic stones have a play of colour similar to that of natural opal, but of a more pronounced or definite nature. The colour appears to emanate from distinct 'patches' which have an angular outline.

*2nd test* — Refractometer. The refractive index of the synthetic is virtually identical to that of natural opal, i.e. approximately 1.45, and may be obtained either from the base of the stone, if flat, or from a domed surface by distant vision technique.

*3rd test* — Microscopic analysis. Close examination of synthetic opal with the microscope will prove it to possess a distinctive hexagonal surface structure, similar to the effect seen on a honeycomb. This pattern covers the entire stone and is perhaps more easily seen when light is transmitted through the stone from beneath. By reflected light, with a light source held above the stone as far as possible, each patch of colour may be seen to consist of the same honeycomb effect, and the abrupt termination of each colour patch, with a tell-tale hexagonal outline, adds to the effect.

By comparison it may be found difficult to 'pin down' the location of the origin of colour in natural opal. When it is found possible to do so, however, the outlines of the colour patches will be seen as either smooth and rounded or as irregular and jagged, and the colour is seen to emanate from streaks, like lightning, totally dissimilar from the honeycombing effect on the synthetic stone. Many synthetic opals so far examined have possessed fairly regular crack-like markings on their surfaces, an effect which is quite distinct.

If the focus is lowered into the stone, when using transmitted light, synthetic opal will in general be found quite free from inclusions, whereas natural stones generally possess some evidence of their natural formation.

*4th test* — Fluorescence. It has been noted that the synthetic opals examined so far have shown no fluorescence under long-wave ultra violet light, whereas, many natural opals fluoresce a cream or whitish colour and also exhibit an afterglow (phosphorescence) when the lamp is switched off. Also some synthetic opals have a tendency to fluoresce a pasty greenish-white under short-wave ultra violet light.

As the production and examination of synthetic opal is still in its infancy, it would be wise not to form any definite opinion as to an opal's origin based on ultra-violet tests alone until further information is available.

*Synthetic Black Opal*

The tests outlined for the identification of synthetic white opal apply equally to the black material with the exception that it is difficult to transmit light through the stone to examine the honeycomb structure, which must be examined with an overhead light source. For the same reason it is difficult to focus into the stone to look for inclusions. The surface effect is even more striking with these stones, however, and little difficulty should be experienced.

## PEARL

White pearls may be separated into four distinct types.
1. Natural (called oriental).
2. Cultured (a bead, normally of mother of pearl, inserted into a pearl-forming mollusc, which deposits a coating of pearl over the bead).
3. Non-nucleated cultured (a type of cultured pearl in which a pearl is caused to grow in a mussel by artificial stimulus without a bead nucleus).
4. Simulated (imitations made from glass or some similar substance often coated with a pearly looking essence).

The following series of tests go only so far towards identifying pearls because the separation of natural from cultured pearls can in general be carried out with certainty only by using expensive equipment normally only available in laboratories.

*1st test* — for separation of simulated pearls.
The pearl may be rubbed gently across the tip of a tooth during which a natural, or cultured pearl will feel distinctly gritty, like a stone, but a simulated pearl will feel smooth like glass.

*2nd test*
Should doubt arise the drill hole should be closely examined with a 10x lens in a good light. Simulated pearls often show wear in this area and the glass bead underneath

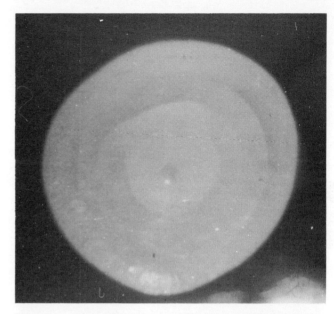

Bisected natural PEARL (above) and CULTURED PEARL (below). The difference between layers of real pearl and the mother-of-pearl bead are obvious

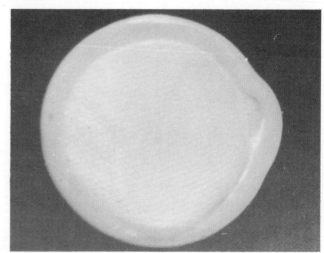

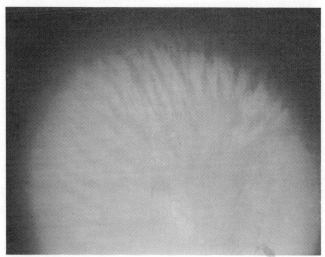

PEARL This is the 'flame structure' seen on the surface of the pink conch pearl

can be easily seen. Failing this careful examination inside the drill hole will reveal the nature of the core.

*3rd test* — for separation of natural, cultured and non-nucleated pearls from each other.

The general appearance of the pearl should be taken into account. Non-nucleated pearls are generally oval in shape, or slightly baroque, and have a distinctive white, smooth lustre. The surface of natural and cultured pearls differs slightly in most cases, cultured pearls having a more transparent lustre, almost waxy, compared with the magnificent lustre displayed by the natural pearl. Cultured pearls often have little markings which always remind the author of mountain ranges on the moon, ridge-like veins.

*4th test* — If held under a bright light source, cultured pearls often give themselves away by the fact that the light travels through the thin outer coating and may be seen to be reflected from the surface of the mother-of-pearl bead nucleus, thereby giving the effect of a sheen.

Under the same conditions it is sometimes possible to see growth line markings from the mother-of-pearl nucleus. These are delicate straight lines, underneath the pearl's surface, running in one direction only, and only seen in certain directions. It is often useful to rotate the pearl while holding it under the light source, when the effect may be viewed to better effect.

*5th test* — The drill-hole of the pearl should be carefully cleaned and then examined, with light aimed at the side of the pearl, which seems to penetrate the stone, giving it a degree of internal illumination. Cultured pearls will have a coating of pearl, often terminated by a thin black line, but in any case showing a distinct ''join'' between the outer coat and the bead. Further down from this point, the drill-hole will be quite smooth. Natural pearls should show regular concentric growth lines.

It must be emphasised that identification of pearls as described above can often separate cultured from natural and quite often indicate that the stones under test are natural, but for any gemmologist to give a 100% guarantee of authenticity to natural pearls without the backing of advanced laboratory tests would be asking for trouble.

Also worth remembering is that just because one pearl in a row has been identified as natural (or cultured) does not automatically mean that all the rest are the same, as mixed rows of natural/cultured pearls are quite common.

# PERIDOT

This gemstone, generally of a lime-green colour with a rather oily lustre, may be identified by the following manner.

*1st test* — Polariscope: Necessary result, double refraction.

*2nd test* — Refractometer.

The refractive index of peridot may normally be obtained at 1.654 for the lower and 1.690 for the higher shadow edge, giving a birefringence of 0.036. Both shadow edges will be seen to move when the stone is rotated on the table of the refractometer. The birefringence is so great that if the back facets of the stone are examined through the stone with the 10x lens or, more easily, the microscope, they will be seen to be doubled. This effect is called doubling of the back facets and is not unique to peridot. It should not be regarded as a test of any great importance.

PERIDOT Brown platelets of biotite, often with angular outlines, are commonly found in peridot. Even more distinctive are the 'water-lily leaf' inclusions; these are tiny crystals of chromite, surrounded by a liquid-filled, crack-like marking that terminated in an irregular circle

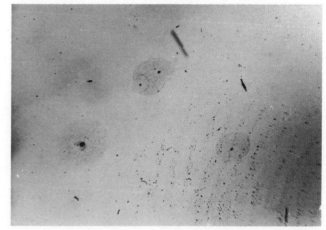

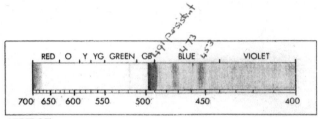

PERIDOT spectrum

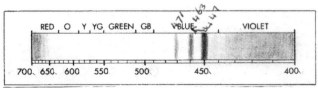

Green SAPPHIRE spectrum

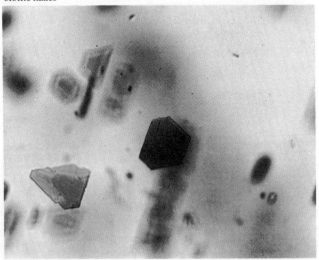

PERIDOT Stones from Hawaii may contain little glass spheres as well as biotite flakes

*Spectrum analysis*

If the absorption spectrum of peridot is examined with the spectroscope three broad bands should be seen in the blue (4930, 4730 and 4530A).

A similar effect may be seen in green sapphire but the bands in the case of peridot are much wider apart, spanning the width of the blue of the spectrum, whereas the sapphire bands are much closer together and vary in intensity, the lowest band being by far the strongest.

If difficulty is experienced in seeing the peridot spectrum, the use of the copper sulphate solution (see Part I) may help. It will be found that if the stone is placed so that the greatest *colour,* not necessarily the greatest amount of light, comes from the stone for analysis, a more distinct effect may be seen. If the stone is oval, or longer in one direction than another, then light should be passed through the longest direction possible.

*Microscopic analysis*

There are a number of inclusions which are quite common in peridot and that are fairly typical of the stone.

111

# PHENAKITE

On rare occasions cut specimens of phenakite, a colourless stone, are encountered. They have quite a distinctive silvery white appearance.

*1st test* — Polariscope: Necessary result, double refraction.

*2nd test* — Refractometer.
A refractive index reading of 1.654 should be obtained for the lower shadow edge, which is the same no matter what the orientation of the stone, and a maximum of 1.670 for the higher shadow, the R.I. of which varies with direction. The birefringence is 0.016.

# ROCK CRYSTAL

Rock crystal is the name given to the common colourless variety of the mineral quartz. The stones possess a watery transparency.

*1st test* — Polariscope: Necessary result, double refraction.

*2nd test* — Refractometer.
The R.I. is 1.54 and 1.55 with a birefringence of 0.009. The lower shadow edge remains in position no matter what the orientation of the stone; the other moves to a maximum of 1.554.

These two simple tests are quite conclusive as there are no other colourless gemstones in this range, but examination of the internal features of the stones can often prove rewarding.

*Other test* — Microscopic analysis. The illustrations show typical inclusions.

ROCK CRYSTAL Needles of rutile or tourmaline, and two-phase inclusions are common

ROCK CRYSTAL Two-phase inclusions

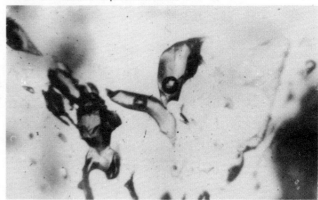

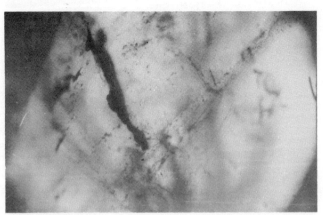
ROSE QUARTZ The internal structure produces many intersecting feathers, which appear to be composed of minute particles

# ROSE QUARTZ

Rose quartz is the translucent pale pink stone often cut as a cabochon, as pendants or small carvings.

*1st test* — Polariscope: Necessary result, double refraction.

*2nd test* — Refractometer.
The R.I. is 1.54 and 1.55 and the birefringence 0.009. If a flat face is available, the full birefringence should be obtained and the lower shadow edge will be found to be static while the upper one varies depending on the orientation of the stone. If the stone is a cabochon, or cut in such a way that the normal refractometer method cannot be used, then the distant vision technique may be adopted and a reading between 1.54 and 1.55 will be obtained.

*Other test*

*Specific gravity*
If the piece under test is large and therefore unsuitable for putting on the refractometer, then a hydrostatic specific gravity test should result in a figure of 2.65.

# RUBY

Ruby, the red member of a family of gemstones called corundum, of which sapphire also forms a part, varies from pale pink to rich blood red of great intensity.

*1st test* — Polariscope: Necessary result, double refraction.

*2nd test* — Refractometer.

A refractive index in the region of 1.77 should be obtained with a birefringence of 0.009. The higher ray will give the same reading no matter what the orientation of the stone, the lower edge will move, but not lower than 1.760.

Sometimes corundum readings are quite indistinct. If white light is used, only a colour fringe at 1.77 may be seen, the shadow which is supposed to engulf the scale of the refractometer below this edge being almost entirely invisible. When using sodium light, the shadow edge is often very difficult to see, particularly with small stones.

If a satisfactory doubly refractive reading is obtained, this proves the stone to be one of the following types:—

1. Natural ruby.
2. Synthetic ruby.
3. Ruby doublet (i.e. stone made with natural blue sapphire top and synthetic ruby base, or even natural ruby top and synthetic base).
4. A freak garnet topped doublet (i.e. a stone made with a thin garnet table fused to a red glass base. It is just remotely possible that one with a doubly refractive garnet top could be found, and must be considered here).

*3rd test* — Examination of the surface of the stone.

The stone should now be carefully examined with the 10x lens for signs of a join mark, which would identify it as some form of doublet. Initially the upper portion of the stone should be looked at, particularly just below the table facet,

GARNET-TOPPED RUBY DOUBLET

GARNET-TOPPED DOUBLET The difference in relief between the garnet top and the blue glass base shows up under a lens

Synthetic RUBY Note the crystals in the garnet top and the bubbles in this plane of focusing in this doublet

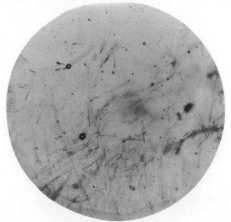

as garnet-topped doublets are made with joins around this area.

When looking for these joins with the 10x lens, the best method is to position the light source and stone in such a way that light is reflected from the facets being examined, towards the eye. In this way, the difference in lustre (surface reflection) between the garnet and glass should be fairly noticeable.

If this examination draws no conclusions the stone should be examined around the girdle, as ruby doublets are generally joined in this area. Obviously when the stone is in a setting this join will be difficult, if not impossible, to find, so that the possibility of the stone being ruby doublet still has to be given consideration in some of the tests that follow.

*4th test* — Examination of the stone by 10x lens whilst immersed.

If the stone is immersed in a liquid (water, xylene, methylene iodide, etc.), against a white background, it will be found very much easier to look into the stone. With 10x lens any of the following features may be seen.

1. The colour may be seen to be in zones or swathes, rather than being evenly distributed through the stone. If the colour can be seen to follow two or three directions, in straight lines, intersecting at an angle of 120°, so that if the pattern were completed throughout the stone a hexagonal form would be the result, this would prove the stone to be, at least in part, natural corundum. If it can be satisfactorily proved that this colour zoning permeates the whole of the stone, then it may be safely identified as natural ruby and no further testing is necessary.

2. If the colour zoning is present but only in the top part of the stone, then the possibility of a doublet still has to be considered.

3. If the colour zoning is of a curved nature, this proves the stone to be partially synthetic, and only the possibility of synthetic ruby doublet needs to be considered.

115

Generally curved growth lines of this type, which are typical of synthetic rubies, are very fine and virtually impossible to see with the 10x lens, so that examination with the higher powered microscope becomes necessary.

*5th test* — Crossed filters.

Should there still be a nagging doubt as to whether the stone consists entirely of ruby material, the possibility of sapphire-topped doublet still being considered, placing the stone between crossed filters will quickly resolve the issue as the ruby should fluoresce bright red whereas a doublet would be inert on the top and glow brilliant red underneath. Careful examination of the effect is necessary, of course, as the non-fluorescing table of natural sapphire can easily be missed.

*6th test* — Microscopic analysis.

The separation of natural from synthetic ruby may be carried out in most cases by microscopic analysis, the presence of any of the features included in the accompanying photographs being distinctive. Synthetic rubies commonly include small bubbles.

*7th test* — Transparency to ultra-violet light.

It has been found that synthetic rubies are more transparent to short-wave ultra-violet light than are natural rubies.

To test the stones, should doubt still exist following the last test, they should be placed table facet down on a sheet of photographic paper, which is immersed in a flat-bottomed dish of water to a depth sufficient to cover the rubies.

This operation must be carried out in a dark room.

The stones should then be exposed for a short time to light from a short-wave ultra-violet light source held about 18 inches above, preferably with other known natural and synthetic rubies for comparison. On developing the paper, images of the natural stones should appear white, exhibiting

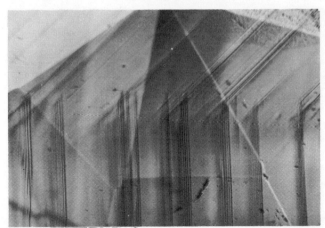

RUBY colour-zoning

RUBY Hexagonal zoning and crystals in a natural stone from Burma

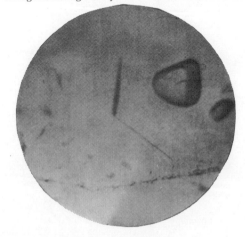

116

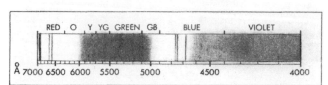
RUBY spectrum

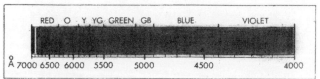
RUBY Fluorescence spectrum

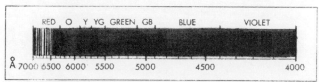
Natural red SPINEL Fluorescence spectrum

their opacity to the ultra-violet radiations, whereas the synthetic stones will appear dark, as they have transmitted the light.

*Other tests*

*Spectroscopic analysis*

Rubies exhibit a distinctive absorption spectrum due to the element chromium.

In the top end of the red are a pair of narrow lines, very close together, forming what is called a doublet (6942 and 6928A). When testing with the spectroscope, all that can generally be seen is a bright line high in the red, which is a fluorescent line, of which more later.

More into the centre of the red are two fainter lines (6680 and 6595A). These may also show as fluorescent lines.

Most of the yellow and green parts of the spectrum are covered by a broad absorption band, and then three narrow lines may be seen in the blue (4765, 4750 and 4685A) before the rest of the blue and the violet is cloaked in further strong absorption.

Unfortunately this spectrum is of no use in the separation of natural ruby from synthetic, as the spectra of the two are virtually identical.

*Crossed filters*

Most rubies, when placed between crossed filters (see Part I), emit a fine red fluorescent glow. This is not a distinctive test as some rubies do not exhibit the glow, whereas red spinels do.

However, if this fluorescent glow is viewed with the spectroscope, an effect called the fluorescent spectra of the stone may be viewed. In the case of both natural and synthetic ruby it consists of one intense bright line in the red, where the doublet appears in the normal spectrum. Spinel, under the same conditions, shows a group of several narrow lines where the red should be.

117

Both natural and synthetic rubies emit a fine crimson fluorescence under long-wave ultra-violet light, although some natural stones show the effect only very weakly. Here again the test is not of great value.

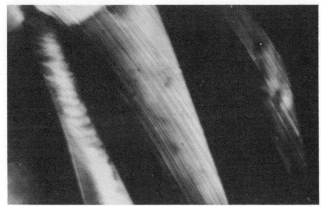

Synthetic RUBY The most common feature is a delicate colour-zoning that resembles the surface of a record. Unlike synthetic sapphires, synthetic rubies require careful examination from every angle while altering the direction of the light under the microscope until the precise angle of reflection is found. Up to thirty minutes at a time should be spent trying to find these lines, when you first start looking at these stones

Synthetic RUBY The bubble is the other common inclusion. Usually today these are very small though sometimes visible under a medium magnification. Also found in tadpole shape, both are to be seen here. Note the little surface cracks from the facet edge near the top left-hand corner; these used to be thought a sign of a synthetic stone as they are caused by careless polishing, however this is no longer so

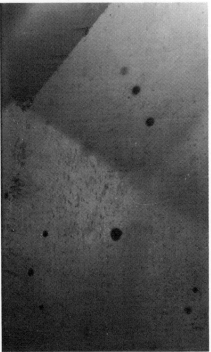

Synthetic RUBY showing curved lines and bubbles

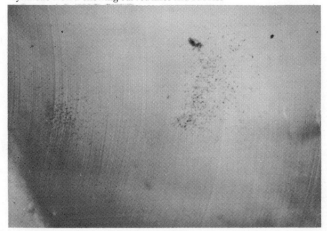

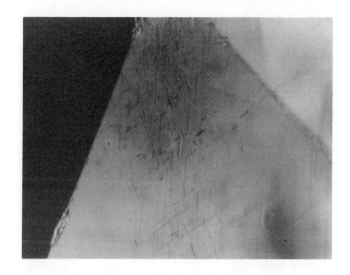

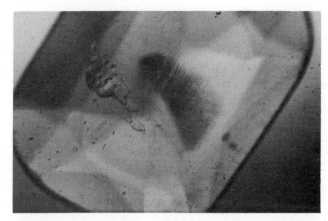

ABOVE LEFT
RUBY Fine needles of any length are a common inclusion, usually intersecting at an angle of 120° producing hexagonals if the effect is complete. From certain directions, the angles do not appear to be 120°. The needles distinguish a natural stone, though many stones only have a few and occasionally only one long one will be found. They sometimes lie near the girdle or back of the stone. Sometimes the needles are so widely dispersed and so small that they only appear under high magnification. They also appear in layers so that the hexagonals only appear by slowly focusing through the stone

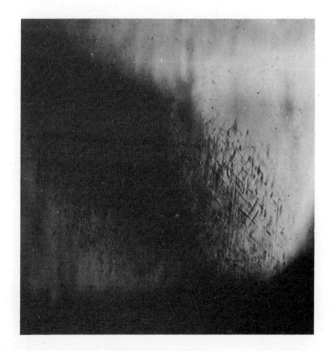

ABOVE RIGHT
RUBY A tell-tale cloud shows up in this stone, it might well be ignored by the uninitiated

RIGHT
RUBY Under higher magnification, the cloud resolves itself into a closely grouped series of short needles

119

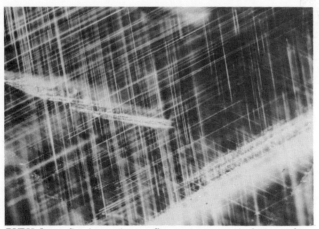

RUBY Long, fine interesting needles are a common inclusion and are known as 'silk' from the effect of their reflections. The stone is from Sri Lanka

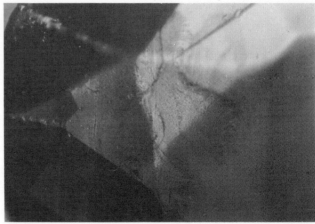

RUBY Fissures that appear to have partially healed are another sign of natural occurrence. More common in sapphires, they are called 'thumb-print' inclusions

RUBY Crystal inclusions, opaque or transparent, are further evidence of natural origin

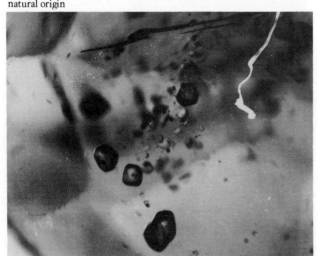

RUBY Another example of natural crystal inclusions

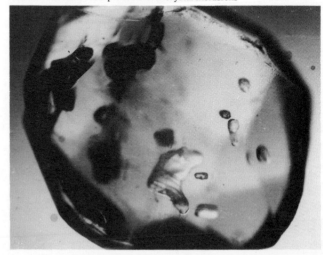

120

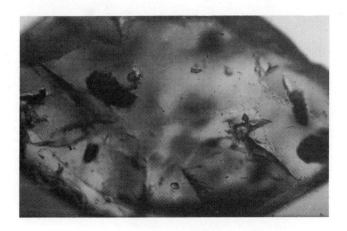

LEFT
RUBY Frequently the crystal inclusion causes a lacy fracture in the host material

BELOW RIGHT
RUBY This crystal appears trapped in a web of its own making!

BELOW LEFT
RUBY A fine example of a group of crystals surrounded by a network of fluid feathers

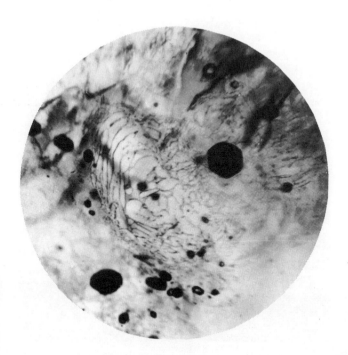

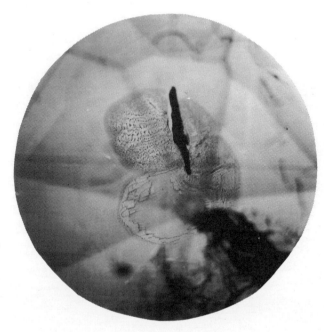

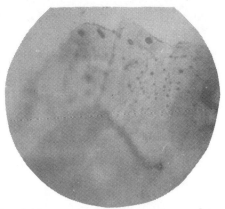

RUBY Rounded hexagonal crystal inclusions in a stone from Thailand. They look like frogspawn

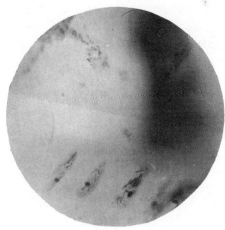

RUBY Rounded opaque crystal inclusions, known as 'turkey feather', in a stone from Thailand

RUBY Tiny grains of metamict zircon have tension haloes in this stone from Sri Lanka

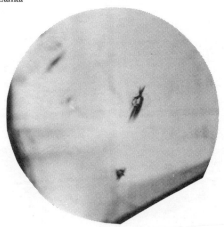

RUBY A two-phase inclusion with hexagonal outline and lacy surround is less typical

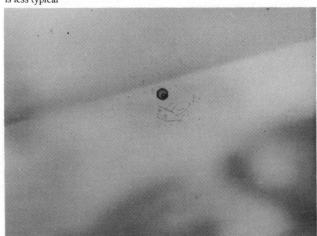

# SAPPHIRE

All members of the corundum family of gemstones other than the red are classified under the name sapphire. The most common colour, and the best known, are the blue and greeny-blue stones so common in modern engagement rings, but other colours, greens, yellows, purples and oranges are fairly frequently come across.

*Blue stones*
*1st test* — Polariscope: Necessary result, double refraction.

With sapphires, the doubly refractive effect is not seen at its best when held table facet down. The best effect is usually obtained with this facet held inclined at an angle of 45° to the polaroids, when the stone is set, or sideways on when loose.

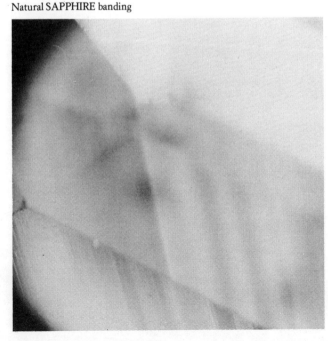

Natural SAPPHIRE banding

*2nd test* — Refractometer.

A refractive index reading approximating to 1.77 should be obtained, with a birefringence of 0.009. The higher shadow edge will be the same no matter what the orientation of the stone, the lower edge will move, and have a minimum reading of 1.760.

As with ruby, it may be found that the shadow is quite indistinct, only the colour fringe that is its termination being seen, so that care must be taken not to miss it altogether.

Provided that satisfactory results have been obtained with the polariscope and refractometer, the stones must be considered to be one of the following types.
1. Natural sapphire.
2. Synthetic sapphire.
3. Sapphire doublet (i.e. a stone made out of a piece of natural sapphire adhered to a base of synthetic sapphire).
4. A freak garnet-topped doublet (i.e. a stone made with a thin piece of garnet fused to a piece of blue glass, the colour of the garnet being drowned by the blue glass).

*3rd test* — Surface examination.

The stone should be carefully examined with a 10x lens for signs of a join, which would identify it as some form of doublet. Initially the upper part of the stone should be inspected, particularly the facets leading up to the table, as garnet-topped doublets are made with joins just around this area.

When looking for these joins, the best method is to position the light source and stone in such a way that light is reflected from the facets being examined, towards the eye. In this way the difference in lustre (surface reflection) between the hard garnet and soft glass should be easily seen.

Once you are satisfied that there is no join mark in this region, the stone should be examined around the girdle, as sapphire doublets are joined there. When the stone is in a setting it is difficult, if not impossible, to reach a satisfactory conclusion to this test, so the possibility of the stone being a sapphire doublet must be kept in mind during some of the following tests.

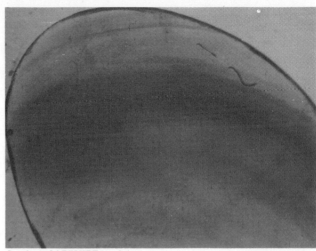

Synthetic SAPPHIRE banding

*4th test* — Internal examination with 10x lens.

If the stone is immersed in a liquid, it will be found very much easier to see its internal features.

RI 1·66 monobromonaphalene

Initially this examination is best carried out against a white background using water or xylene. The following features are distinctive.

1. The colour of the stone may be seen to be in zones or swathes, instead of being evenly distributed throughout the stone. If the colour is seen as a curved band, this will prove the stone to be, at least in part, synthetic sapphire. In contrast to ruby, the colour zoning in synthetic sapphire is best seen with 10x lens and less clearly under a microscope, as the banding is much more broad and distinct.

2. The colour may be seen to be in straight lines or bands, often intersecting at angles of 120°, in two or three directions, so that if the pattern were completed throughout the stone, a hexagonal form would result. Colour banding in

SAPPHIRE doublet with natural sapphire top and synthetic ruby base

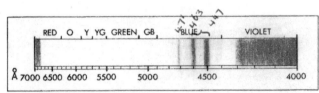
SAPPHIRE spectrum showing all three bands

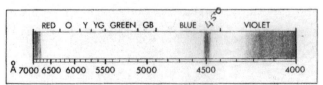
SAPPHIRE spectrum showing only the 4500 line

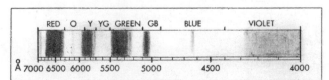
GARNET-TOPPED DOUBLET spectrum

one direction, providing that it can be proved to be straight (do not forget that curved bands, looked at from certain angles, will appear as straight) will prove the stone to be natural sapphire, if only in part. If the straight banding permeates the whole stone, it may be safely identified as natural sapphire and no further testing is necessary. If the banding is in the top of the stone only, then the possibility of sapphire doublet remains.

*5th test* — Microscopic analysis.

The inclusions to be found in sapphires commonly provide conclusive evidence as to the stone's origin.

Most of the remarks and photographs of inclusions included under the section devoted to identification of natural ruby also apply to natural sapphire and reference should be made to those photographs, in particular the first three, as short intersecting needles are a very common occurrence in sapphires and an invaluable aid to identification. More pictures are to be found below.

*6th test* — Spectrum analysis.

Should there still be an element of doubt as to the stone's identity, the spectroscope can prove very helpful with sapphires.

Natural sapphires often (not always) show an absorption band in the blue at 4500A. Sometimes one or two weaker bands may be seen to the left of it (4600 and 4710A).

When the 4500 band is seen, it proves the stone to be natural, at least in part, as synthetic sapphires do not show these bands.

For the sake of completeness it is worth mentioning that garnet-topped doublets often show a spectrum which consists of three broad bands towards the red end of the spectrum owing to the glass base of the stone. Sometimes the garnet top provides three further bands in the centre of the spectrum producing quite a rich effect.

It should be remembered that a sapphire doublet may well

show the 4500 band owing to the natural sapphire top section of the stone.

*7th test* — Short-wave ultra-violet light.

Should there still be an element of doubt as to whether the stone is natural, synthetic or sapphire doublet, the use of short-wave ultra-violet light can prove of great help.

Most synthetic sapphires show a whitish-blue fluorescence, or a peculiar surface effect similar to particles of dust sprinkled on the stone. Further, when carefully examined while fluorescing it is often possible to pick out curved banding, which it is not possible to see under normal conditions, proving the stone to be synthetic.

A sapphire doublet is likely to stand out under the short-wave lamp, as the top part of the stone, when examined from the side, will be inert, while the bottom shows synthetic fluorescent effects.

The test for the sapphire's fluorescent effects under short-wave ultra-violet light is not fool-proof, as some natural stones show fluorescent effects, but it may be said that:—

a. Any stone showing fluorescence must be considered suspect.

b. Any stone showing fluorescence at its back only is extremely suspect.

c. Any stone showing curved banding is positively synthetic.

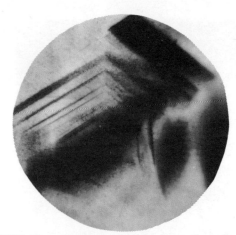

SAPPHIRE  The zonal arrangement of the short rutile needles emphasizes the hexagonal architecture of the host stone

SAPPHIRE  Two radio-active zircon inclusions

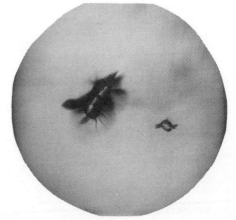

126

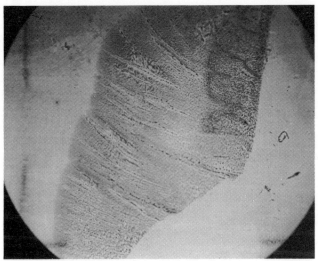

SAPPHIRE This 'fold' inclusion, typical of Burmese stones, is a partially healed fracture filled with many undigested fluid droplets

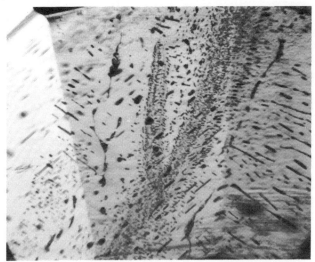

SAPPHIRE Another example of a fold inclusion in a Burmese stone

SAPPHIRE A close study of a partially healed fracture show that it consists of many two-phase inclusions

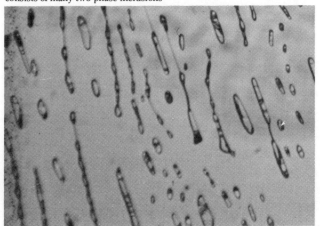

SAPPHIRE This thumbprint inclusion seems to be the only evidence of this stone's natural origin; it is sufficient

# SINHALITE

The colour range of this mineral is from yellow-brown through golden-brown to greenish-brown.

*1st test* — Polariscope: Double refraction.

*2nd test* — Refractometer.
The RI is 1.67 and 1.71; birefringence 0.038.
A careful refractive index reading should be sufficient to identify the stone, but as the birefringence is similar to that of peridot, confusion sometimes results.

*3rd test* — Spectroscope.
The absorption spectrum of sinhalite is also similar in general appearance to peridot, but on closer inspection it will be seen that there are four lines in the sinhalite spectrum, and that they are narrower than the peridot bands.

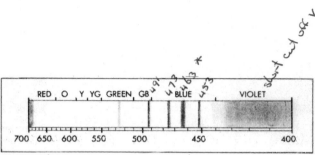

SINHALITE spectrum

*Other test*

*Dichroscope*
Sinhalite exhibits distinct pleochroism, the colours seen being pale brown, green brown and dark brown.

# SPHENE

Sphene is so rarely found in pieces transparent enough to be cut, and is so soft anyway that its use in jewellery is impractical. It is very rarely found except in collections. The colour is generally yellow, brown, or green. The stones, when cut, exhibit a very strong fire, in excess of diamond, although the deeper the colour the less obvious it is.

*1st test* — Polariscope: Necessary result, double refraction.

*2nd test* — Refractometer.
No reading will be seen as the refractive index (1.90—2.02) is too high for the refractometer.

*3rd test* — 10x lens.
Very strong doubling of the back facets should be seen, far in excess of zircon's and peridot's, due to the wide bi-refringence.

*4th test* — Spectroscope.
The stone should have a weak didymium spectrum of a group of fine lines in the yellow, generally seen as a weak band. The other group of lines normally associated with this spectrum, in the green, should be too weak to be seen.

*5th test* — Dichroscope.
Sphene possesses distinct pleochroism, the colours seen through the dichroscope being greenish-yellow, reddish-yellow and virtually colourless, depending on the direction of viewing the stone.

# SPINEL

Natural spinel is rarely seen in jewellery by reason of the fact that the beautiful red stones are hardly ever found in pieces good enough and large enough to cut and the blue stones, which are reasonably common, are of an unattractive colour, generally tending towards a dirty violet shade.

However, spinel is made synthetically in vast quantities, occasionally red but more commonly blue and colourless.

The identification of spinel, dealing with both natural and synthetic stones, will be described one colour at a time.

## COLOURLESS SPINEL

Natural colourless spinel is virtually unknown so need not be considered, but synthetic colourless stones are so common, used in particular for setting into relatively cheap gold eternity rings and occasionally as an imitation of diamond, that serious consideration as to methods of identification must be given.

*1st test* — Polariscope: Single refraction but often showing anomalous double refraction effect.

*2nd test* — Refractometer (if possible). 1.727

*3rd test* — Ultra-violet light.
Under long-wave ultra-violet light, synthetic colourless spinel shows a weak greenish fluorescence while the short-wave lamp produces a vivid white, almost blue-white, effect. This fluorescence is distinctive for the stones and provides a valuable testing factor for small gems set in eternity rings where a refractometer reading is impractical.

Colourless spinel is used for doublets with a coloured cement imitating other gem stones. Immersion in water will disclose the deception.

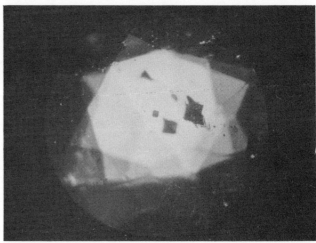

SPINEL Opaque octahedral crystal inclusions are typical of spinel; they can appear in series or unrelated to each other

Synthetic SPINEL Showing the cement junction of the coloured material between the colourless top and bottom sections, this synthetic doublet is suspended in oil

130

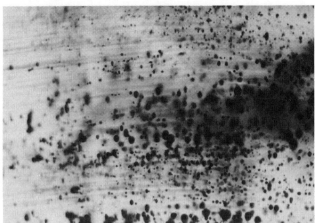
Synthetic red SPINEL These normally contain many gas bubbles in combination with curved growth lines

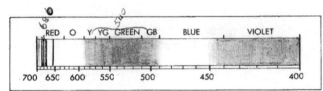
Red SPINEL spectrum

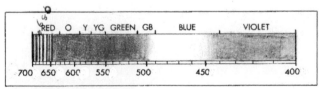
Red SPINEL spectrum showing copper sulphate

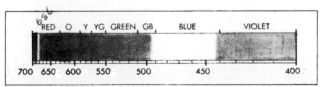
Synthetic red SPINEL spectrum using copper sulphate

# RED SPINEL

Both natural and synthetic red spinel are known, but far from common.

*1st test* — Polariscope. Single refraction but synthetics often show anomalous double refraction.

*2nd test* — Refractometer. Natural 1.720. Synthetic 1.727.

*3rd test* — Microscopic analysis.
Both natural and synthetic stones possess inclusions which are typical and in most cases separation of one from the other is fairly easy. The photographs show examples of the internal features most commonly found.

*4th test* — Spectrum analysis.
Natural red spinel has a broad absorption band which covers most of the yellow and part of the green, and the brighter coloured stones exhibit a number of fine lines in the red, so that the spectrum bears a resemblance to that of ruby with the exception that no lines appear in the blue.
If the spectrum is examined when light from the copper sulphate solution is used to illuminate the stone, the spectrum takes on a more distinctive appearance. In the red may be seen a group of fine fluorescent lines against a dark background, far different from the single strong line seen in the ruby spectrum.
Synthetic red spinels do not show this multiple fluorescent effect, but simply a single line in the red at about 6860A. This is similar to the ruby spectrum, but there are no lines in the blue of course.

*Other test* — Fluorescence
Both natural and synthetic red spinels exhibit a red fluorescence under all three types of radiation.

# BLUE SPINEL

The colour of natural blue spinels is such that they are rarely called upon to take a place in a piece of jewellery, the rather slaty-blue shade being of an unattractive nature. The synthetic stones however are quite magnificent, too good in fact, and generally recognisable on sight.

*1st test* — Polariscope. Necessary result, single refraction.
But the synthetic stones generally exhibit anomalous double refraction.

*2nd test* — Refractometer.
Synthetic blue spinels have a fairly constant refractive index of 1.727 but the natural stones may vary from anything between 1.715 to 1.754 so that there is the possibility of finding a natural blue spinel with a synthetic spinel R.I.

*3rd test* — Spectroscope.
The natural blue spinel spectrum is rich and distinctive. The strongest and broadest band is in the lower-blue area (4590A); two other bands, almost as broad, are in the orange and yellow (6320 and 5820A) whilst narrow lines of varying intensity may be found in the yellow-green (5550A), lower green (5080A), mid-blue (4780A) and two in the violet (4430 and 4330A). Patches of weaker but broader absorption in the yellow-green and blue areas only serve to enrich the spectrum.

The synthetic blue spinel spectrum is due to the colouring element cobalt and in general appearance the same as the cobalt glass spectrum. Three broad bands may be seen in the orange, yellow and green.

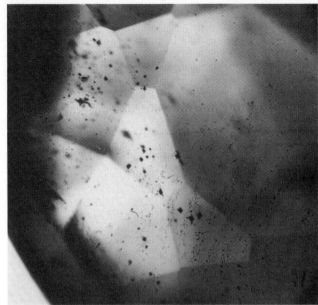

SPINEL  The series of inclusions on the right are typical of these stones

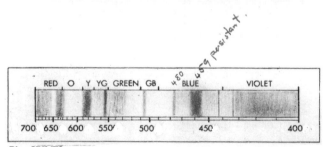

Blue SPINEL spectrum

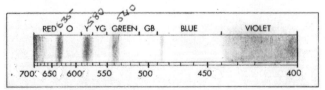

Synthetic blue SPINEL spectrum

132

*Chelsea colour filter*

Synthetic blue spinels turn red when viewed through the Chelsea colour filter. Natural blue spinel also shows a hint of red through the filter but nothing like the vivid colour of the synthetics.

*Fluorescence*

Between crossed filters and under long-wave ultra-violet light, many synthetic blue spinels appear red.

Under the short-wave lamp, synthetic blue spinels appear a fairly vivid greenish-blue and exhibit an effect similar to synthetic sapphires, which is like a coating of white dust on the stone.

## OTHER COLOURED SPINELS

Violet, purple and mauve spinels are quite commonly found and, very rarely, green spinel.

Synthetic stones are produced in many colours, most importantly yellow and green.

Polariscope, refractometer, and microscope will identify these types in most cases. The anomalous double refraction of many synthetics, higher refractive index (1.725 to 1.728 for synthetics as against 1.715 to 1.720 for most natural stones) and presence of inclusions in the natural stones provide plenty of evidence.

In addition, it may help to remember that synthetic yellow spinels fluoresce green under both long-wave and short-wave ultra-violet light and that synthetic green spinels may either fluoresce red under long-wave or green under short-wave lamps.

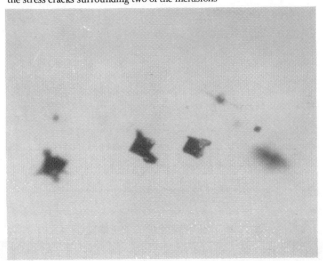

Mauve SPINEL More octahedral crystals in natural mauve spinel. Note the stress cracks surrounding two of the inclusions

# SPODUMENE

Spodumene may be seen in a number of colours, the most popular being the pale pink stone, called kunzite. Yellow and yellow-green stones are possible whereas the emerald green variety called hiddenite is a great rarity.

*1st test* — Polariscope: Necessary result, double refraction.

*2nd test* — Refractometer.

A refractive index reading of approximately 1.660 and 1.675 should be obtained with birefringence 0.015.

A satisfactory refractometer reading should be enough to identify the stone but a few other interesting phenomena are worth nothing.

### Other tests

*Dichroism*

The pink and green varieties of spodumene posses very strong dichroism, particularly noticeable in kunzite when taking into account its pale colour. The effect may be seen without the use of the dichroscope by viewing the stone in various directions and noticing that it is colourless down certain of them and pink down others.

*Spectroscope*

The emerald green hiddenite exhibits a spectrum due to the element chromium, which is the cause of its colour. Fine lines may be seen in the red combined with a broad absorption band across the green.

*Ultra-violet light*

Under long-wave ultra-violet light, kunzite exhibits a pink or orange fluorescence, the effect being less strong under short-wave lamps.

STAR DIOPSIDE

# STAR STONES

Most star stones may be identified by obtaining a distant vision refractive index reading. Most care is required when dealing with sapphires and rubies as these are also made synthetically.

Brief descriptions of likely encountered star stones are given in order of ascending refractive index.

Glass imitations are made with four or 6-rayed star effect by engraving intersecting lines on the back of the stone and covering this with a metallic substance, thereby causing a reflective effect. The R.I. of these can be anywhere between 1.45 and 1.70.

| | | |
|---|---|---|
| 1.55 | Rose quartz | Pale rose-pink with 6-rayed star. Sometimes provided with a reflective backing to enhance the effect. When examined under a single light source a reflection of the light bulb may be seen in the centre of the stones. |
| 1.56-1.58 | Beryl | Occasionally star emerald has been found. |
| 1.66-1.67 | Kornerupine | Green 4-rayed star. |
| 1.68 | Enstatite | Green 6-rayed star. |
| 1.67-1.70 | Diopside | Black 4-rayed star; rays caused by short needles intersecting obliquely. |
| 1.72-1.75 | Spinel | 4- or 6-rayed star possible, green, green-blue to black. |
| 1.76-1.77 | Ruby and Sapphire. | 6- or 12-rayed star in red, blue grey, etc. |

Synthetic rubies and sapphires normally show a star effect which is too good to be true. The only sure method of identi-

Pale natural
STAR SAPPHIRE

Synthetic
STAR SAPPHIRE

fication is to examine the stone under the microscope while immersed in a liquid, or even with the 10x lens. Natural stones generally include distinct hexagonal colour zoning in straight lines whereas the synthetics contain bubbles and curved colour banding.

Star rubies and sapphires made synthetically by Linde Air Products normally have a letter L in the back of the stone.

Four- or six-ray garnet star stones (R.I. between 1.74 and 1.81) are quite common. Analysis of the colour by spectroscope generally reveals absorption bands typical of almandine garnets.

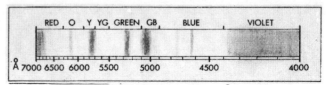

ALMANDINE GARNET STAR spectrum

# TOPAZ

Topaz is known to the public almost exclusively as a yellow or sherry-brown stone, but in actual fact it may also be found colourless, blue, green, and pink. The last colour is rare in nature, most pink stones on the market being heat-treated yellow stones.

*Yellow and pink topaz*
*1st test* — Polariscope. Necessary result, double refraction.

*2nd test* — Refractometer. 1.63-1.64 (0.008).
There are a number of gemstones with refractometer readings in this area so great care is needed to measure the birefringence very accurately, then reference may be made to the following confirmatory tests.
*Confirmatory test 1.* — Long-wave ultra-violet light.
Certain of the yellow and sherry brown stones emit an orange-coloured fluorescence when tested under long-wave ultra-violet light.
*Confirmatory test 2* — Microscopic analysis.
Topaz frequently contains typical inclusions.

*White and blue topaz*
*1st test* — Polariscope: Necessary result, double refraction.

*2nd test* — Refractometer: 1.61 — 1.62 (0.010).

Yellow TOPAZ These often contain thin, liquid-filled cracks which reflect light totally, thus appearing opaque and black

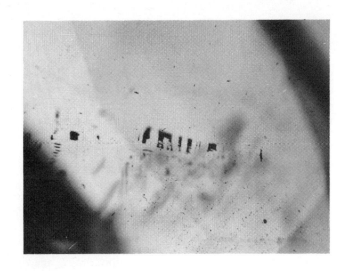

LEFT
Yellow TOPAZ  A smaller group of liquid-filled fissures

BELOW LEFT
TOPAZ  White and blue stones often contain two-phase inclusions that stand out in relief

BELOW RIGHT
TOPAZ  More usually in blue and white stones, these two-phase inclusions have a flat transparent appearance

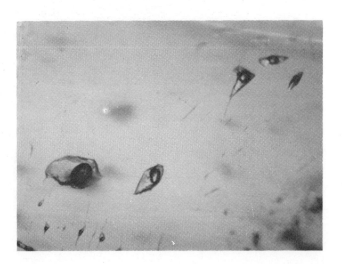

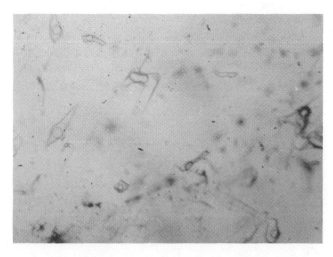

# TORTOISESHELL

Translucent to opaque, mottled yellow and brown, tortoiseshell (actually made from the shell of turtles) may be identified by microscopic examination of its surface. In true tortoiseshell the brown markings may be seen to be composed of many tiny brown speckles, whereas in the imitations, generally made of one of the synthetic resins, the markings are due to colouring agents which show a uniform, well defined edge through the microscope.

TORTOISESHELL This disc-like structure is typical of real tortoiseshell

Imitation TORTOISESHELL Only a straight colour swirl can be seen in this imitation piece

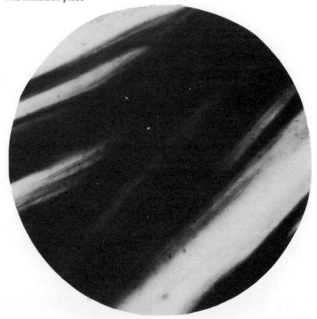

# TOURMALINE

Tourmaline is one of the few gem species that may be found in virtually any colour. The best known is the transparent green which may vary between dark to light in strength of colour.

*1st test* — Polariscope: Necessary result, double refraction.

*2nd test* — Refractometer.

A refractive index between 1.62 and 1.65 should be obtained with a birefringence from 0.016 and 0.022. The average R.I. is 1.620 to 1.638. The upper shadow edge will give the same reading no matter what the orientation of the stone; the lower edge varies with direction.

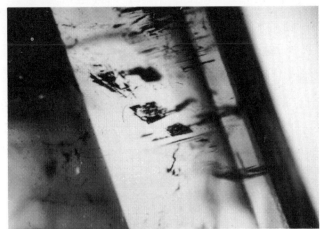

TOURMALINE The most distinctive inclusions are the 'trichites' or irregular canals filled with liquid. These only appear opaque from certain angles

TOURMALINE  A typical pattern of trichites

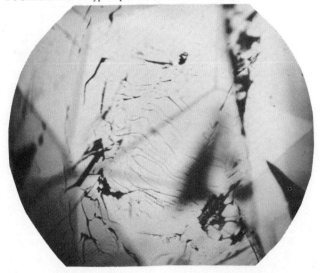

TOURMALINE  This tadpole two-phase inclusion is also quite common

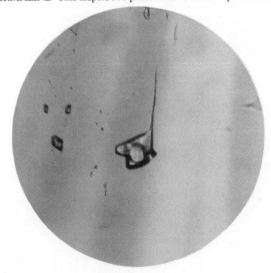

*Doubling of back facets*

Although the birefringence is not as great as peridot and zircon, it is often possible to observe doubling of the back facets with the lens or microscope. The effect may not be seen in dark green or brown stones as one of the rays is absorbed.

Most tourmaline shows very strong dichroism so that the colour along one direction may be seen to be much deeper than that down directions at right angles to it. In the darker coloured green and brown stones, the tourmaline will appear black in one direction.

*Microscopic analysis*

There are a number of inclusions typical to the stone, as seen in the photographs.

# TURQUOISE

Turquoise is opaque, waxy looking, pale blue to pale green-blue material which is generally cut in the cabochon form.

*1st test* —Refractometer.

The distant vision technique will have to be employed and a reading of about 1.60 to 1.62 should be obtained. Any prospective turquoise with readings exceeding these should be viewed with the greatest suspicion.

*2nd test* — Surface examination.

Careful examination with the 10x lens and microscope will reveal the distinctive surface structure of turquoise. The lustre has been described as waxy, i.e. a rather soft greasy looking texture, and it often possesses a rather uneven polish, whereas glass, plastics, and certain other imitations have a smoother and brighter polish.

Upon close examination, the colour may be seen to be composed of a pale blue background with speckles of white all over, and it should generally be possible to find some small black or brown vein markings on the stone.

Gilson ''synthetic'' turquoise, under close inspection, has a whitish background with tiny angular blotches of blue colour distributed evenly across it, so making distinction from the natural stone possible.

*3rd test* — Spectroscopic examination.

If light reflected from the surface of genuine turquoise is analysed with the spectroscope, an absorption band in the blue (4600A) which is fairly diffuse and weak, and a line in the violet (4320A), which together form quite a distinctive spectrum, may be seen.

Satisfactory results with all three tests will be evidence enough to identify the stone as turquoise but care should be taken not to rely on any one test alone, as small pieces of real turquoise bonded together could give a natural spectrum and/or even possibly a similar refractive index.

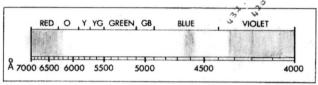

TURQUOISE spectrum

# ZIRCON

With practice, the identification of zircon is one of the quickest and easiest of tasks. Stones of this species may be found in most colours, but it is well to remember that the popular colourless and pale blue stones used in jewellery are heat-treated reddish-brown stones. A dirty, oily green and reddish-brown are the most common natural colours.

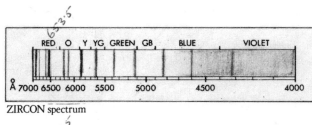

ZIRCON spectrum

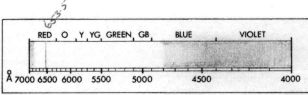

ZIRCON spectrum

ZIRCON The doubling of the back facet edges, as seen through the table of the stone

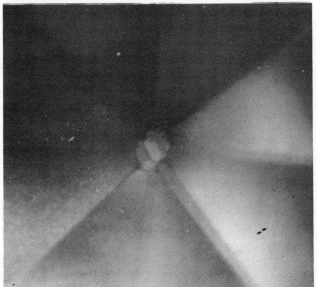

*1st test* — Spectrum analysis.

The typical absorption spectrum of zircon consists of a series of narrow lines, fairly evenly spaced across the complete spectrum.

The strongest of these is in the red (6535A) and is present in almost every zircon. In fact the colourless, pale blue and pinky-brown zircons often only show this absorption as a very fine line.

No other gemstone possesses an absorption spectrum likely to be confused with that of zircon. As the refractive index of the stone is too high for a normal refractometer, and as there are few distinctive inclusions to be found, the distinctive spectrum is an essential gem-testing property.

*Other tests*

*Doubling of back facets*

The birefringence of zircon is so great (0.059) that if the back facets of the stone are examined through the table facet with the aid of either the 10x lens or microscope, strong doubling of the back facets should be clearly seen.

*Ultra violet light*

Great care must be taken when subjecting zircons to ultra-violet radiations, as the colour of the stone can alter if left under the lamp for any length of time.

Many zircons will be found to fluoresce a mustard yellow colour, some weakly, some quite strongly, under both long and short-wave lamps.

143

# ZOISITE

Extremely fine blue to violet blue transparent stones come from Tanzania, many of which are heat-treated from material which is naturally coloured green, yellow, pink, brown, and khaki. The natural colours are rarely placed on the commercial market because of their unattractive appearance.

*1st test* — Polariscope: Necessary result, double refraction.

*2nd test* — Refractometer: 1.691 — 1.700 (0.009).

*Other tests*

*Spectroscope*
    A broad absorption band may be seen in the yellow-green (5950A) with a fainter band in the green (5280A) and another in the blue (4550A).
*Dichroscope*
    Very strong trichroism may be seen through the dichroscope, the colours being blue, purple, and green.

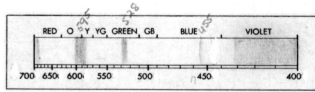

ZOISITE spectrum

144

# APPENDIX

## Average Refractive Indices

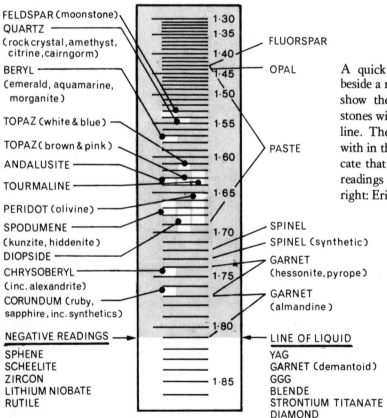

DOUBLY REFRACTING

(Rotate stone to obtain maximum D.R.)

FELDSPAR (moonstone)
QUARTZ
(rock crystal, amethyst, citrine, cairngorm)
BERYL
(emerald, aquamarine, morganite)
TOPAZ (white & blue)
TOPAZ (brown & pink)
ANDALUSITE
TOURMALINE
PERIDOT (olivine)
SPODUMENE
(kunzite, hiddenite)
DIOPSIDE
CHRYSOBERYL
(inc. alexandrite)
CORUNDUM (ruby, sapphire, inc. synthetics)

NEGATIVE READINGS

SPHENE
SCHEELITE
ZIRCON
LITHIUM NIOBATE
RUTILE

1·30
1·35
1·40
1·45
1·50
1·55
1·60
1·65
1·70
1·75
1·80
1·85

SINGLY REFRACTING

FLUORSPAR
OPAL
PASTE
SPINEL
SPINEL (synthetic)
GARNET (hessonite, pyrope)
GARNET (almandine)
LINE OF LIQUID
YAG
GARNET (demantoid)
GGG
BLENDE
STRONTIUM TITANATE
DIAMOND

A quick guide to refractive index identification, for use beside a refractometer. Doubly refracting stones, on the left, show the approximate birefringence on the scale. Those stones with a higher reading than 1.81 are shown *below* this line. The singly refracting stones, on the right, are dealt with in the same way. Where there are two lines, these indicate that the R.I. can vary approximately between the two readings for different stones of the same material. (Copyright: Eric Bruton)

# TABLE OF THE AVERAGE REFRACTIVE INDICES OF THE PRINCIPAL GEMSTONES

## GROUP A — SINGLY REFRACTIVE GEMSTONES

| | | |
|---|---|---|
| Fluorspar | | 1.434 |
| Opal | | 1.45 |
| Glass | Between | 1.44 and 1.70 |
| Spinel | | 1.715 |
| Synthetic Red Spinel | | 1.715 |
| Other Synthetic Spinels | | 1.727 |
| Zinc-Rich Natural Blue Spinel | Between | 1.715 and 1.750 |
| Pyrope Garnets | Between | 1.73 and 1.76 |
| Almandine Garnets | Between | 1.76 and 1.80 |
| Rhodolite Garnets | Between | 1.745 and 1.760 |
| Spessartite Garnets | Between | 1.78 and 1.81 |
| Y.A.G. | | 1.834 |
| Demantoid Garnets | | 1.89 |
| G.G.G. | | 2.02 |
| Blende | | 2.37 |
| Strontium Titanate | | 2.41 |
| Diamond | | 2.418 |

## GROUP B — DOUBLY REFRACTIVE GEMSTONES

| | | |
|---|---|---|
| Iolite | | 1.537 — 1.547 (0.010) |
| Quartz | | 1.544 — 1.553 (0.009) |
| Beryl | Between | 1.56 — 1.59 (0.003 — 0.009) |
| Topaz (White and Blue) | | 1.610 — 1.620 (0.010) |
| Nephrite | | 1.62 approx. |
| Topaz (Yellow and Pink) | | 1.63 — 1.64 (0.008) |
| Tourmaline | Between | 1.62 — 1.65 (0.016 — 0.022) |
| Danburite | | 1.63 — 1.64 (0.006) |
| Apatite | | 1.63 — 1.64 (0.003) |
| Andalusite | | 1.634 — 1.644 (0.010) |
| Peridot | | 1.65 — 1.69 (0.036) |
| Jadeite | | 1.66 approx. |
| Phenakite | | 1.65 — 1.67 (0.015) |
| Enstatite | | 1.66 — 1.67 (0.10) |
| Kornerupine | | 1.66 — 1.68 (0.012) |
| Spodumene | | 1.66 — 1.68 (0.015) |
| Diopside | | 1.67 — 1.70 (0.030) |
| Sinhalite | | 1.67 — 1.71 (0.038) |
| Zoisite | | 1.69 — 1.70 (0.009) |
| Idocrase | | 1.70 — 1.71 (0.005) |
| Epidote | | 1.73 — 1.77 (0.034) |
| Chrysoberyl | | 1.745 — 1.755 (0.009) |
| Sapphire and Ruby | | 1.76 — 1.77 (0.008) |
| Benitoite | | 1.75 — 1.80 (0.047) |
| Scheelite | | 1.92 — 1.94 (0.017) |
| Zircon | | 1.93 — 1.99 (0.059) |
| Sphene | | 1.900 — 2.020 (0.120) |
| Lithium Niobate | | 2.21 — 2.30 (0.09) |
| Synthetic Rutile | | 2.610 — 2.897 (0.287) |

# INDEX